KNOWLEDGE AND
THE FUTURE OF MAN

INITIATING THE SESQUICENTENNIAL
OF SAINT LOUIS UNIVERSITY
1818–1968

KNOWLEDGE AND
THE FUTURE OF MAN

AN INTERNATIONAL
SYMPOSIUM

❖

EDITED BY

WALTER J. ONG, S.J.
SAINT LOUIS UNIVERSITY

HOLT, RINEHART AND WINSTON
NEW YORK   CHICAGO   SAN FRANCISCO

TO ALL THOSE
WHO FROM THE BEGINNING
HAVE CONTRIBUTED
TO MAN'S GROWTH
IN KNOWLEDGE
AND UNDERSTANDING

✤

CONTENTS

[vii]

PREFACE

K NOWLEDGE AND THE FUTURE OF MAN is a theme touching both the future itself and the present, which prepares for the future. The theme relates also in a special way to the past in the collection of studies offered here. The year 1968 marks the sesquicentennial of Saint Louis University, the oldest university in the United States west of the Mississippi River, which has chosen this theme, Knowledge and the Future of Man, to unify the symposia and other academic events celebrating its sesquicentennial. As a prelude to these events, through its Committee for the Sesquicentennial, the university has planned the present book for the general public under the conviction that this same theme is of great interest far beyond the university and the academic world as a whole.

The distinguished scholars contributing to this collection thus write not merely for Saint Louis University but for the world. The studies here are all original works, done especially for this sesquicentennial volume, where they are now printed for the first time. Each contributor addresses himself in his own way to the general subject of Knowledge and the Future of Man in terms of his own field of competence and special interests.

Saint Louis University was founded by Bishop Louis William Du Bourg as Saint Louis Academy "for young gentlemen" in 1818, when the City of St. Louis was a pioneer settlement of some three thousand people. In 1828 it was placed under the direction of the Society of Jesus (informally known as the Jesuit order), a Catholic religious order of men committed largely to educational work since shortly after its founding in 1540. The State of Missouri was admitted to the Union in 1821, and in 1832 the Missouri General Assembly granted the first university charter west of the Mississippi to the trustees, all members of the Society of Jesus.

Grown to an institution with thirteen different faculties or schools, seventy-seven departments, and nearly twelve thousand students, in 1967 Saint Louis University became the first American Catholic university to reconstitute its board of trustees with a majority of laymen and a lay chairman. The university proposes to grow further still as a great Catholic educational center to which the Society of Jesus continues its full commitment with the increased stress on lay responsibility and ecumenical sharing particularly favored since the Second Vatican Council. The fourth half-century of the university dawns at a propitious time, when the knowledge explosion to which the intellectual developments of the past have led offers all universities opportunities to discharge responsibilities in teaching and research and in civic, national, and global cooperation with even more devotion and success than in the past. The present volume salutes what lies ahead.

WALTER J. ONG, S.J.
For the Committee for the Sesquicentennial
Joseph J. Simeone, Faculty Chairman

St. Louis, Missouri
January, 1968

I

THE ENVIRONMENT OF
LEARNING

1

KNOWLEDGE IN TIME

WALTER J. ONG, S.J.

Saint Louis University

M AN IS A VENTURE in knowledge. The story of knowledge and its uses, good and bad, is the story of man. Man's knowledge is essentially incremental. It not only accumulates but also metabolizes and grows, feeding on other things and on itself. Its potential is unlimited, which means that when it is true as true can be, and certain beyond the shadow of a doubt, it is also incomplete.

This book is concerned with what happens as knowledge grows and what will happen as man puts his increasing knowledge to use in the future.

Knowledge did not always grow so fast as it does now. Its growth has accelerated from an extremely slow start. Insofar as quantitative statements about knowledge have meaning, we can be fairly certain that there was a time toward the beginning of man's history when knowledge took 10,000 years—perhaps even 100,000 years—to double, and that at a later period it doubled in 1000 years, and still later in 500 years. It has been estimated that today man's knowledge doubles every 15 years. We are used to this tempo of development of knowledge and find it hard to believe how slowly knowledge advanced before the development of writing. In

[3]

some stone-age cultures, the same pattern for a hand axe or spear point persisted for thousands upon thousands of years. In such cultures massive social and psychological structures evidently almost immobilized knowledge.

But virtual immobilization was necessary. It insured against loss. Before the invention of writing (only some 5500 years ago, around 3500 B.C.) knowledge was not only in short supply but also devastatingly insecure. In cultures without records, it could easily leak away. Gargantuan efforts were needed simply to conserve knowledge by keeping it fixed either through recitative formulas for such knowledge or, for nonverbalized knowledge, through such cultural institutions as the tradition of unvarying ˙spear-point design. Without writing, mere retention of the knowledge that had accumulated (no one knew quite how) proved so formidable a task that even apart from the risk of loss if set patterns were varied, the subsistence economies of early mankind could afford neither the time nor the energy for planned knowledge expansion. This state of affairs persisted to a greater or lesser degree for centuries after the invention of writing and even beyond the invention of print until the implications of print for storing and shaping knowledge were digested into the social consciousness and individual psychological structures.

Until print was thus interiorized, cultures remained largely what David Riesman has well labeled "tradition-directed." In such cultures, when expansion of knowledge actually did occur, it was likely to pass with little notice. Thus medieval European thinkers, for example, went far beyond Aristotle in the development of formal logic, moving toward modern symbolic logic (though without the symbols or variables of modern logic, so that the movement was all the more arduous). But they appear to have been aware hardly at all that they had made vast new discoveries. The essential intellectual need was still felt to be holding onto what was known. Eric Havelock's intriguing *Preface to Plato* and Frances A. Yates's seminal work on *The Art of Memory* have made it clear how early world views and thought structures inherited from antiquity and still widely operative as late as the seventeenth century were in great part determined by the need to hold knowledge in patterns that served ready recall. You knew the things that lent themselves to memory schemes.

Memorization and the iconographic imagination, which memorization encourages, constituted a style of life. The Ramist "method" or way of abstractly organizing knowledge and communication, which swept the most technologizing parts of Europe in the sixteenth and seventeenth centuries, was in great part a tantalizingly simple memory system, disguised as science and made plausible by diagrams that could be given ready currency by print. The method proved short-lived, for the new invention of printing, which Ramism exploited, was actually making mnemonic systems in the mind less necessary, as our various computing machines have finally made them obsolete. Knowledge storage was effected more and more outside the mind, first by writing, then by print, finally by our electronic circuitry. But those living through the changes induced by new knowledge storage and retrieval and communication developments are never entirely aware of what the changes are. Hence of necessity they lean on obsolescence and even find obsolescence exciting.

For the advancement of learning, storage of knowledge is essential, but insofar as knowledge is mere "information" or "structure" its storage and retrieval are not truly intellectual tasks. As artificial extramental information storage and retrieval systems (writing, print, and electronics) evolved, the mind was freed more and more to do its proper work of thinking, and the acceleration of knowledge got under way. To store and organize knowledge, oral cultures had to devote vast amounts of time to reciting it. Learning *was* in effect memorizing. Early chirographic cultures recorded knowledge and began to analyze it. Late chirographic cultures, such as that of medieval Europe, codified it. The typographical culture of the Renaissance indexed it; indexes were not unknown in manuscripts, but they remained relatively inefficient until print could produce hundreds of copies of a text with all the words in exactly the same place on the page, at which time indexing became a major selling point for learned works. Today we have computerized knowledge, which is to say that not merely have we set up outside the mind exponentially more effective information storage and retrieval systems but also, more basically, that we are actually breeding knowledge outside the mind. The computer is a special milieu in which knowledge can be cultivated outside its normal habitat.

Of course, the computer breeds knowledge only insofar as knowledge involves structures of "information"—that is, insofar as it can be quantified, directly or indirectly. This means that the computer can do almost anything with knowledge except think about it, which is to say it can do everything but decide with reference to an actual, existing situation whether something is true or false. An actual, existing situation is always one in which there are nonquantified and even nonconceptualized factors. It is, in other words, a noncomputerized situation. Computer verdicts concerning "truth" or "falsity" are vacuities. Either before or after they are arrived at, they have to be applied by someone who *really* knows. But the computer frees the mind to apply knowledge (to judge truth and falsity) in many situations more complex and sweeping than any the mind could compass without computerization.

Not only do new knowledge storage, retrieval, and communication systems (the "media") accelerate the growth of knowledge, but the growth of knowledge also of course accelerates the development of new media. Scripts grow out of the knowledge accumulated in oral culture, the alphabet out of greater knowledge accumulated in a pictographic script culture, alphabetic letterpress typography out of structures of knowledge favored by a chirographic or manuscript culture, and electronic circuitry out of the vast store of knowledge which typography made possible and put at the service of modern science.

When we look to the speed with which the media develop, we find that here, too, there is a spectacular acceleration. Only after being on earth some 500,000 years (to take a fairly good working figure) did man move from his original oral culture, in which written records were unknown and unthought of, to literacy. The first script appeared around 3500 B.C. In another two thousand years the alphabet put in its appearance, around 1500 B.C. By the mid-1400s of the Christian era alphabetic letterpress printing appeared in west central Europe. In another four hundred years the telegraph was devised. Within another sixty years, the wireless. Thirty-five years more brought television. A few decades later we had the whole panoply of spacecraft, Telstar, electronic computers in vast quantity, and countless related devices. Each advance exploited antecedently existing knowledge more efficiently than had the advances that went before, for new knowledge does not simply layer itself onto existing knowledge but interacts with it. It is not an additive but a multiplier.

The total pattern of acceleration in knowledge is thus a complex one. Of itself, knowledge grows and accelerates its own growth. This growth also produces new media, which further accelerate growth (and of course change the structure of knowledge and of the psyche, as will be seen later). The new media themselves, finally, appear in an accelerating sequence, more and more of them faster and faster as time moves on.

II

We have reached a period today when the accumulation of knowledge has made possible insights of new clarity and depth into the history of knowledge itself. Growth of knowledge soon produces growth in knowledge about knowledge, its constitution, and its history, for knowledge is of itself reflective. Given time, it will try to explain not only the world but itself more and more.

What has happened and is happening to knowledge can be considered under several more or less distinct headings: (1) growth in knowledge of the physical universe; (2) growth in knowledge of man and his life world, including his sense of history; (3) increased exteriorization of knowledge (connected with the development of "objective" science); (4) interiorization of knowledge; (5) thrust into the future and growth in responsibility; (6) the permanent limitations of growth. We can take these up in order.

KNOWLEDGE OF THE PHYSICAL UNIVERSE

When marveling about growth in knowledge, many persons focus immediately on our increase in knowledge of the physical universe during the past hundred years (since Darwin) or perhaps three hundred years (since Newton). Here results of increased knowledge are indeed striking. Discoveries in the physical sciences often lead to the production of "hardware" or other products that are highly visible and palpable and that enable man to dominate his physical environment spectacularly: steam engines, telegrams, radar, jet-propelled spacecraft, plastics, television. Knowledge is power. In the early 1600s Francis Bacon gave this old commonplace its best publicized utterance, and Thomas Hobbes soon reiterated Bacon's cosmopolitan Latin in plain English. But Bacon and Hobbes only stated the aphorism. We have lived it, particularly regarding the physical sciences.

Even at his imaginative best, early man could not quite foresee what we have lived through. Bacon had thought of better organizing or "methodizing" the knowledge already on hand and of exploiting nature by achieving a better grasp of "forms." He hardly conceived of breaking through the kinds of frontiers that Newton, Darwin, and Planck have put behind us.

The breakthroughs began with two seventeenth-century developments: the application of mathematics to the physical sciences and an intent and minute observation of nature unknown to earlier ages, which, contrary to the still popular persuasion, had not consciously thrown out induction in favor of deduction but had simply supposed that ordinary observation sufficed for inductive purposes and which thus had not troubled with controlled experiment. Anyone could tell immediately that a heavy body "naturally" falls faster than a light body because when stones and feathers were thrown out a high window at the same time, the stones reached the ground first. Despite Newton's laws of gravitation, they still do.

Experimentation to prove they do not or should not had to do less with ordinary experience than with pure science. But physical science seldom stays pure, and the new sciences in the seventeenth century and later made themselves felt in practical ways very soon. Indeed, post-Newtonian science was in alliance with practical craftsmanship from the very beginning. The closely controlled observations called for by the new mathematization and experimentation themselves demanded finely constructed tools, such as telescopes and microscopes and vacuum pumps. The new sciences used knowledge-producing tools more than earlier science had ever done, and it was a natural thing for the artisans who could make delicate machines for research purposes to make scientifically designed machines for practical purposes. A new breed of thinker arose, the "inventor." "Projectors" the eighteenth century still called them disdainfully, with little sympathy for the Thomas A. Edison syndrome.

We have long ago passed the stage where "inventors" seem intruders on the intellectual scene. The physical sciences have paid off in practical contrivances and processes so abundantly as to make us even discredit science that does not have immediate application. Systematized, formalized knowledge has penetrated the whole of life. In a technologized society not only automobiles and television sets but even soap and apples cannot be produced effectively without a store of systematized, formalized knowledge. Artisan's rule-of-thumb skills have largely yielded to science and are yielding more and more daily.

The result has been a new texture for life itself. Man is dealing constantly with complex, formalized structures rather than with "nature," whether it be in planting corn specifically designed for his region's rainfall and temperatures or crossing a neighborhood street intersection, which he must do by following traffic lights programmed to the city-wide diurnal flow of traffic. It is misleading to imply, as Jacques Ellul and others do, that these formal patterns are something alien to man, a self-subsistent intrusion on his life. They are in fact very human structures devised by human beings in order to make their lives bearable, to give them more security, privacy, and personal independence than early man ever knew. (Philippe Ariès has shown in *Centuries of Childhood* how lacking in security, privacy, and independence were living conditions for even the well to do through the eighteenth century and later. The crowding in our slums today was normal to earlier urban life; it has become intolerable because now for the first time it can be avoided and indeed is avoided by most city dwellers.)

It is not the inhuman effects of technological living—our being "dominated" by machines, whatever that may mean—but the human effects that pose our problem. The science that underlies technological living has given a new shape to the contents of the human mind. In earlier ages abstract, formalized thought was dominantly philosophical and religious. Knowledge of the physical universe, while it was not so thin as the popular impression today would have it, was still relatively jejune and unsatisfying. Today the physical sciences have become so rich and fecund that the mind can lose itself in them for a lifetime.

The mere bulk of learning in the physical sciences is overwhelming. Devising systems to abstract, store, and retrieve the results of each year's new research has become a major problem. Even with the best of such systems, it is occasionally less time consuming to repeat certain bits of research than it would be to comb the vast float of extant literature for needed information.

The overwhelming weight of detailed knowledge regarding the physical world carried within technological cultures calls for a special balance in man's consciousness as he learns to address himself and the world around him. Technological man has a personality structure different from that of nontechnological man. The stages of culture described by David Riesman as successive tradition-directed, inner-directed, and other-directed are relevant here. Technological man may be inner-directed or other-directed or on the border line between the two, but he cannot be tradition-directed as primitive peoples are. (This is by no means to say that technological man has no traditions; he does have them in great number, but he is also likely to reflect on them and analyze them.) To move a nontechnologized culture into the scientific, technological world demands far more than supplying those in such a culture with "information." It demands a restructuring of personality which inevitably forces the painful psychological, political, and ideological dislocations seen in the developing countries today. We can hope to understand and to deal with these dislocations better than we now do. But we can hardly hope to eliminate them totally.

Meanwhile, it is defeatist to suppose that man's attention to the physical world is some kind of degradation. There are dangers here, of course, dangers of total absorption, but of itself man's present managerial position over some of the natural world (some of it only, a tiny fraction, for there is no question of managing the galaxies) means that the material world is being more spiritualized by being more subjugated to the mind.

KNOWLEDGE OF MAN AND HIS LIFE WORLD

If advance in the physical sciences has been spectacular, it has, nevertheless, in fact not been conclusively greater than advance in knowledge elsewhere. A little attention to library acquisitions and bibliographies today as compared with 150 or even 10 years ago makes it patent that insofar as increments in various knowledges are comparable, the humanities and the social and behavioral sciences are growing seemingly as fast as the physical sciences. By far, most of the intellectual and literary and cultural history on library shelves today had not been written 150 years ago. A hundred and fifty years ago most of our linguistic knowledge concerning the thousands of languages man speaks or has spoken did not exist. Neither did most of sociology, anthropology, psychology, and countless other subjects dealing with the human life world as such.

Moreover, in these fields knowledge often grows geometrically because here, perhaps more than in the physical sciences, different and even remote areas of knowledge have a way of interacting with one another today to form new and productive configurations. Psychology and linguistics yield the composite field of psycholinguistics, itself closely allied to cultural anthropology. Analysis, especially historical analysis, of literary forms, of scientific discoveries, of styles in painting, and of political institutions daily throw more and more light on one another.

In addition, the humanities are automatically enlarged by growth of knowledge in the sciences. Every science, not only the social and behavioral sciences, has a history, which is a matter for humanistic study. And the humanities seize on technological interventions for their own specific purposes and thus extend themselves into new areas. Opposition between technology and the humanities is more imaginary than real. The printing press, a technological device, was developed largely under Renaissance humanist auspices, and the use of computers for textual study and other humanistic purposes is already becoming commonplace.

Advances in the humanities and social and behavioral sciences have combined with advances in the physical sciences to affect radically man's sense of his life world and sense of identity, if we take sense of identity to mean the sense of where one comes from and how one relates to those other than oneself, how one fits into what one knows of the universe.

Changes here have been too vast to enumerate, but some of their forces can be seen in the changes regarding man's sense of time. Until quite recent years man had no very effective idea of the real time scales applying to the universe of which he was a part. Today our frames of reference have been brought more into accord with actuality, the macroscale frames largely by the natural sciences and the (relatively) microscale frames by the humanities and social sciences. We know that it took the universe some five to ten billion years of active evolution to produce the conditions making life possible on our earth. We know that social structures and psychological structures have evolved irreversibly over periods of tens of thousands and hundreds of thousands of years. Even though it is not always explicitly attended to, the past is a massive fact in the sense of identity of any well-educated man today, that is to say, of any man thoroughly in touch with his surroundings. We no longer think of ourselves as beings who inhabit a cozy (but savage) universe that began some 6000 years ago, as Western man often used to do, nor do we think of time in terms of unreal cyclic patterns such as the Hindu kalpa (4,320,000,000 years), an imaginative projection having nothing to do with researchable fact and indeed running counter to such fact. Today we know the past as something with which we are in publicly and circumstantially verifiable contact, and as affecting the real present in ways that are matter for scientific, cosmological, and historical study.

The immensity of space has likewise lately become known to us and affected our sense of identity, but it has done so less directly, for space is mostly beyond us, in a real sense. If and when man gets to the moon, he will be roughly only 1/400 of the distance to the sun and an infinitesimal fraction of the distance to the nearest star outside the solar system. Most of space is permanently remote from us. We feel little kinship with Betelgeuse or with galaxies millions of light years away. But time is in us: the material in our own bodies is five to ten billion years old. Our modern sense of measured time has revolutionized all knowledge dealing with man's life world at least as drastically as Planckian and Einsteinian discoveries have revolutionized modern physics. The appearance of studies such as Martin Heidegger's great work entitled *Being and Time (Sein und Zeit)* signals the overwhelming sense of time in which modern man is plunged. From antiquity man has speculated philosophically about the nature of time, but only in recent generations have his philosophy and his whole life world become immersed in it. This immersion in time is what commits modern man to change and propels him irresistibly into the future.

Knowledge concerning man and his life world, which includes his artistic and literary productions, also is power, quite as much as knowledge of physical science is. It is most obviously power in the social and behavioral sciences, which lend themselves readily to use, moral or immoral as the case may be, aiding in the solving of human problems or implementing manipulations of human beings as though they were things. Knowledge in the humanities is power, too, for the humanities give us greater insight into the nature of man, and this insight provides ground for greater control over man's behavior, again for good or evil. To understand a people's psychology in order to deal with them on a practical footing, it is advisable to study their literature and art. Such study can be undertaken more productively today than ever before because of the immense advances, effected over the past few generations, in comparative literary and art history and in criticism.

Humanistic knowledge grows in complex fashion because what is new mixes constantly with what is very old. The humanities draw directly on knowledge that is rooted in prehistory, and even the newest discoveries in the humanities are likely to have antique counterparts: psychological literary criticism may draw on Freud's description of the Oedipus complex, but Freud himself is rooted in Euripides, who in his drama put his finger directly on Freud's problem two thousand years earlier. Still, Euripides is not Freud. Freud knew more, even about Oedipus, and so does the competent present-day critic. Even when we fully avow how much our present knowledge of man derives from the ancients, we must still be aware that what we today know about man in terms of his whole life world immeasurably exceeds what earlier man could get at. We have the advantage both of the general accumulation of learning and also of the greater penetration of time and space which has made cross-cultural studies possible.

EXTERIORIZATION OF KNOWLEDGE

As knowledge has grown, it has become both more exteriorized and more interiorized. Early man's knowledge tended to merge the exterior and interior worlds. Even in a technologized culture, the child's consciousness must first be formed in an intersubjective world of personal relationships —mother, father, other human beings. Primitive man remained close to this world in his adult cosmology, too. The universe was anthropomorphic in a myriad of ways. Lonely for his own kind on an earth that was underpopulous, early man commonly filled the empty forests and air and waters with living beings—wood nymphs, gnomes, spirits of all sorts, nereids—not entirely unlike himself. Totemic systems blended the animal and human in ways that still enchant and puzzle anthropologists and philosophers down to Maurice Merleau-Ponty and Claude Lévi-Strauss. Even so sophisticated a cosmology as that of Aristotle and Ptolemy was basically animistic and anthropomorphic: the putative celestial spheres surrounding the earth and bearing the planets were taken to be living, intelligent beings. Only through their mediation did change take place in our dull sublunary world. We can see these early constructs of physical science as partly projections from man's own interior, minimally "objective." They connect in part with early man's proclivity for interiorizing, auditory syntheses (the music of the spheres) rather than objective, visual syntheses (the universe held together by measurements).

At the same time, early cultures often exteriorized man's own interior to a degree that would make us acutely uncomfortable. Tribal patterns of thought and activity overpowered the individual. Visitors from technologized cultures living with the people in nontechnologized society often find themselves unnerved by the almost total lack of privacy: life is lived as a kind of total exposure, with almost no opportunity for withdrawal into oneself. Of course, before writing was invented, individual study of a subject was impossible. Thought advanced either obscurely in the gradual evolution of social institutions and language or by being publicly talked out, which is to say it advanced communally. Oral cultures had no Aristotles or Scotuses or Newtons or Einsteins. To a degree, morality itself consisted in external arrangements: touching a dead body even inadvertently could render one ritually impure and vaguely guilty, even though it was not strictly a prohibited action.

Post-Copernican, post-Newtonian man has in great part (not entirely, as he often thinks) foresworn allegiance to these primitive views that half-humanized and thus half-interiorized the external world and at the same time half-exteriorized man's interior consciousness. The interior and exterior are thought of as separate—all too much so, particularly since Plato and Descartes. The external world is now conceived of more typically as a visual synthesis, a set of things defined by surface, a congeries organized not by sound and resonance but by a certain structured disposition in space, something essentially picturable. Although the world in which we live presents itself to all the senses, we habitually consider it as something that is, above all, seen, and perhaps touched (but here only to a degree: touch works for stones but not for clouds). Essentially, the world is "objects," things with surfaces abutting on one another. Our knowledge has progressed, in the physical sciences particularly, when we have thought of the world only this way, keeping ourselves and all interiority out of the focus of attention. Technology has to do with objective things, apprehended from outside, devoid of personal resonance. Eventually, our knowledge has become focused on exteriority so intently that we have tended more and more to regard man himself and perhaps even God as a thing. We are by now acutely aware of the corner we have been painting ourselves into. We talk incessantly of the dangers of depersonalization. We fear being reduced to a mere Social Security number, a computerizable quantity.

INTERIORIZATION OF KNOWLEDGE

But all the while that knowledge was in a sense being exteriorized and depersonalized, a counter movement has also been under way. Ours is not only an exteriorizing, depersonalizing age but also an interiorizing, personalizing one. No other age has been so explicitly conscious of the human person as ours is. Although early society was deeply personal in some ways, its organization communal and feudal, based on personal ties rather than on issues and analytically conceived programs, it was also in other ways terribly impersonal, and unavoidably so. Often it showed little respect for human life. Capital punishment for crimes such as stealing or even for what we would consider misdemeanors took a staggering toll every day in the most civilized countries of Europe as late as the sixteenth century and beyond, when crowds comparable to those attending professional baseball and football games today still regularly assembled to view hangings and the subsequent savage mutilation of the body of the victim (drawing and quartering) carried out, in accordance with the law, before the victim expired. Punitive mutilation was common: one met on the streets men and women whose ears or noses had been cut off or who had been branded for punishment. In this general context of unprogrammed and programmed violence, religious persecution, which strikes us today as so horrible when seen in isolation and which was indeed horrible enough, shows itself also as almost incidental —a manifestation in one particular life area of patterns of savagery accepted everywhere.

In such a world it is not surprising that philosophical thought, too, attended relatively little to the person as person. The good life of the Greek philosophers simply wrote off the slaves and lower classes as not worth consideration. The higher ranges of speculation in the Greek tradition were largely concerned with "forms" and grew much more directly out of the physics of the time than out of explicit attention to the humane. The term "metaphysics," that is, post-physics, which was used for the highest reaches of philosophical thought, suggests the general state of affairs. Deep interest in the human as human was of course discernible in philosophy from the start, but when abstract thought moved in on man's life world, somehow or other it atomized this world into a congeries of virtues and vices. The richness of human life was caught in something of its integrity by early art and literature, but even here, we are now beginning to understand, the economy of knowledge inherited from primitive oral culture tended to dissolve human complexities in abstract virtue-and-vice polarities. Oral modes of thought persisted long after the arrival of writing and even print, losing their dominance only when the romantic movement overwhelmed the ancient rhetorical and dialectical educational tradition.

Major intellectual developments focusing explicity on the person as person can be traced directly to early Christian theology in the first ecumenical councils through the Second Council of Constantinople (A.D. 553), as Denis de Rougemont has suggested in *Man's Western Quest*. Here the early Church thoroughly thrashed out problems concerning the person of Christ and the difference between Father, Son, and Holy Spirit precisely as persons, further elaborating the Scriptural insistence on the personal relations of each individual human being to God. Philosophy, however, picked up little of the theological concerns centered around the Trinity of Persons. Only in the nineteenth century (that is, during the industrial revolution) did philosophy become highly anthropologized, centering itself more explicitly on man as man. In our own day this anthropologizing has culminated in the personalist philosophy of Gabriel Marcel, Karl Jaspers, and others. Personalist philosophy (and complementary reverse personalism, such as Sartre's) are just as typical of twentieth-century civilization as technology is.

Interiorizing, personalizing trends in thought are too diffuse and too numerous to be listed here in detail, but something of what they come to can be seen in the history of of literature. Literature of course always personalizes its matter in the sense that it has somehow to do with man in his lived experiences, with human problems and hence with the interior, human consciousness. But its personalizing potential has been progressively intensified as the focus of plotting has moved over the ages from the more exterior world of fixed social institutions, exteriorized adventure, or episodic exploit, to the human interior directly realized through stream-of-consciousness or interior monologue and related techniques. Such a movement can be traced variously in Greek tragedy from Aeschylus through Euripides, in Elizabethan drama from its crude para-academic beginnings through Shakespeare, or again in the history of the novel, which in two centuries evolved from the relatively exteriorized machinations of Fielding's eighteenth-century *Tom Jones* to the baroque interiority of Joyce's twentieth-century *Finnegans Wake*. Indeed, the novel itself as a genre comes into being late because it depends on advanced interiorization of attention, if we accept Lionel Trilling's well-founded view that a novel is essentially a critique of a complex society which sees through the obvious, exterior, somewhat fraudulent surface of that society to some deeper (interiorly realizable) truth. As a personalized critique of society, though far less interiorized than Joyce, Fielding's work is more interiorized than is John Lyly's *Euphues* of nearly two centuries earlier.

Something similar to what has happened in literature has

also happened in art, as José Ortega y Gasset has explained in *The Dehumanization of Art and Other Essays:* the focus has moved from representations of the exterior world to more and more concern with representations of inner states of mind. Obvious parallels suggest themselves in music.

Perhaps the most pervasive interiorization of knowledge today is coming about in our understanding of history. In place of what used to be more or less standard history, consisting of accounts of military and political ventures, we are developing a sense of history as basically cultural and psychological. We know now that psychological structures change as cultures change: much of the current popular interest in the "media" feeds on a vague awareness of this fact, which has been the concern of scholars quite clearly since Freud's *Civilization and Its Discontents* and indeed from the time of Giovanni Battista Vico (1668–1744). External historical events are shaped by personality structures, which themselves are the result of external historical events and cultural patterns, all these interacting with a certain amount of incalculability insofar as free human decisions (always in very limited existential fields) are also in play.

To the best of modern historians the world is not simply a series of external happenings so much as it is a concatenation of interior states of consciousness: both exterior and interior need to be accounted for, but the principal focus is on the latter. Personalist philosophies of intersubjectivity have their effect here in showing how interpretation of exterior reality itself demands and builds on relations of persons to persons. The Jesuit paleontologist and cultural historian, Pierre Teilhard de Chardin, has gone further in interpreting personal, interior consciousness as the focus of the entire evolutionary process, cosmic, organic, and historical. In *The Phenomenon of Man*, in *The Future of Man*, and in others of his works, Teilhard attends to the way the physical universe evolves toward "inwardness" and consciousness and to the way consciousness itself evolves as man fills and organizes the earth.

Looking to historiography in these perspectives and with the eyes of the future, we might say that history is deposited as personality structure. You and I in our own particular consciousness are our own history, and collectively we are the history of mankind. History is the way we are. It is why we confront ourselves and other men and the world the way we do. To say this is not to imply any kind of fatalism or total determinism. Man is free, and history itself involves free choice. But man must make choices within situations that are actually presented to him and that he does not choose. History is a fabric woven by choice out of necessity. In such a fabric, choice regards the present and the future. The necessities, interior as well as exterior, in which choice asserts itself often derive from the past.

What we are beginning to learn about the effects of history in the organization of consciousness and personality structures has almost limitless implications for our understanding of knowledge itself and its development. For knowledge exists in dependence on given personality structures. A tradition-directed culture cannot produce highly original speculative thought because the personality structured to such a culture cannot function independently of accepted tribal patterns and, indeed, cannot even want to experience itself as "original." Tradition-directed cultures are, roughly, oral cultures or cultures in which script has not been sufficiently interiorized to change psychic organization. Eric Havelock has shown in his *Preface to Plato*, mentioned earlier, how Plato's highly speculative philosophy, and in particular his "ideas," were dependent on an attitude toward the world made possible only by writing, which prepares the psyche for the fixity and remoteness from the human life world that the "ideas" stand for.

Our growing awareness of the variant psychological structures produced by different cultures and in particular of the need for knowledge to be detribalized in the sense of personally interiorized (as in David Riesman's "inner-directed" character) in order to produce a technological thinker is affecting our sense of global understanding. We are reaching the point where we may no longer regard "elections" in which a predictable winner piles up 99 percent of the vote as frauds managed so naïvely as to be merely quaint. We can begin to appreciate that such more or less enforced patterns of publicly manifested conformity found in neotechnological cultures are doubtless due in great part to old tribal or tradition-directed personality structures, which cannot be eradicated in a day. The divisions of opinion on which a democracy thrives could paralyze a personality formed in a newly technologized or half-technologized milieu, in which the older tribal organization of consciousness calling for nondeviance is still operative.

We are also, or should be, long past the stage where we label members of still earlier, pretechnological, oral cultures "lazy" because their members do not take enthusiastically to the ethic of "hard work" which technological cultures automatically structure into their successful members' psyches. We know that persons in pretechnological cultures are perfectly capable of doing things that are quite as difficult and demanding as the tasks of an assembly-line worker or a junior business executive but that their outlook on existence is at root so communal that the idea of "making something of yourself" will necessarily appear to them unrealistic and even unmanly. Man, they feel, is supposed to live in a world of human events, not in constant traffic with such things or abstractions as technological life demands. To make a fetish of work is to dehumanize oneself, to become a machine. The problem facing developing nations, as an increasing number of psychological studies shows, is not a problem of exhorting lazy people to work hard, but more profoundly, that of restructuring personalities or of structuring young, forming personalities in the ways that technological life requires for its members if they are to survive as human beings. Our growing knowledge of knowledge is making us more adept at describing socially determined differences in personality structures. But we are as yet far from knowing how to change them.

THRUST INTO THE FUTURE AND GROWTH IN RESPONSI-BILITY

The growth of knowledge is certainly one of the factors thrusting modern man into the future. Very primitive peoples tend to live from hand to mouth more than more developed civilizations do. Growth into a planned economy has come about gradually. Manufacture of clothing and weapons showed planning for the future, which the planting of crops further intensified. Later the large civil governments developed in antiquity relied on intensive planning, as in the elaborate irrigation work along the Nile in ancient Egypt. At first governmental planning had been largely to maintain the precarious status quo, but with colonization and empire it meant also plotting major changes for individuals and regions, though seldom avowed changes in style of life. Yet even in style of life, some programmed change was possible as early as among the ancient Romans, for example, because these peoples had enough knowledge of climate, natural resources, engineering (particularly for their roads), and writing (an absolute essential, as Harold Innis has made clear) to have some control over the future.

Today, however, programming the future has entered a new stage. Earlier time scales, related more or less to the duration of a few generations, have been superseded. We think habitually of the future of the human race on earth a hundred years from now, or five hundred years, or two thousand years. In the control of natural resources—the soil and its products, food crops, forests, fisheries, water power—we already effectively plan in ways that will determine conditions of life in the next few centuries, and it is in part our ability to do this which gives our life the future pitch it has. But the principal reason for the thrust into the future which makes our state of mind today different from that of earlier man is our knowledge of cosmic and organic evolution. We are aware that we live in an evolving universe, pitched into the future. The world is structured in patterned change. Not only can man change things; he can change the very pattern of change as well.

Our awareness of patterns of development extends beyond the exterior universe into knowledge itself. As time goes on, we learn more and more about how knowledge comes into being, about learning processes and processes of discovery, about how knowledge can be not merely stored and communicated but also brought into existence as well as increased. We engineer knowledge itself in advance, as the Rockefeller Foundation helped do a few decades ago when it found the increment of knowledge in the life sciences inadequate and hence made the decision to divert large funds into stepping up the increment here, a decision that helped produce within a few years our new understanding of DNA and the genetic code of living organisms. The ability to program knowledge gives man a kind of exponential control over nature. If knowledge is power, knowledge of how to generate knowledge is power over power.

With his present sense of an evolving universe, his store of knowledge, and his awareness of knowledge as power, man today quite naturally feels his life role to be largely that of a manager. Of course, not every man and woman even in a highly technologized society thinks of himself or herself as an active global planner, but everyone knows that this is now the role of the human race taken as a whole. From national planning commissions of all sorts down to science fiction and comic strips, the mythology of global and, to a very limited extent, cosmic management permeates all levels of society and all economic levels.

We know that if we are responsible today more than ever before for the conditions we live in, we shall also be still more responsible in the future. In the past when civil disorders occurred or wars broke out, man could put it down to the inescapable state of human affairs, to vices bred into men. No one in his right mind would deny that today we have our share of real vices, but we are at the same time aware that breakdowns in society must be accounted for by a great many things other than vice—lack of education, of economic opportunity, the revolution of rising expectations, the unthinking use of the mass media of communication, and a great many other social developments over which we can exercise control even though we may not yet have learned how to do so very effectively.

The buildup of knowledge and the proliferation of means for storing and communicating knowledge that makes man's managerial role possible and imperative also, of course, creates severe strains in society. There is a great deal of illusion in loose talk about "turnover" in knowledge, which mistakes knowledge for a commodity and thus confuses it with agglomerates of "information," forgetting that true knowledge in human beings cannot "replace" earlier knowledge but must somehow be integral with earlier knowledge in order to be functional or even psychologically possible at all. Nevertheless, even when we write off the cheap equations such talk relies on, we must still note that the rapid increase in knowledge divides the generations. The mode of assimilating the store of human knowledge, and particularly the "image field" used in managing it, probably differs considerably between those who are twenty years old and those who are fifty. Such differences should not be minimized. But neither should they fill us with despair. They are not unbridgeable but simply take work to bridge. A good many persons in their fifties and beyond are doing the best work interpreting just such differences between the generations. It is paradoxical that only a relative oldster such as Marshall McLuhan can interpret the younger generation to themselves and that to many of his own generation his interpretation remains incomprehensible. It would be more paradoxical if all the younger persons understood and none of the oldsters did. Such is not the case. Some of both groups do. His interpretations and those of others like him in fact do bridge the chasm.

A more serious problem created by proliferation of knowledge and man's resulting managerial responsibility is that of withdrawal. Withdrawal symptoms show up more and more in technologically advanced societies. Often they are factitious and even meretricious: the beatnik or hippie is not really "dropping out" but looking desperately for an in-group that will satisfy his own demands. Often, seeming withdrawal is merely a way of securing attention without responsibility. Nevertheless, it creates real problems, and the withdrawal syndrome is certainly connected with the pressures of managerial expectations. The sociological studies show that hippies come typically not from the underprivileged but almost entirely from among the relatively well to do or the very wealthy, where the pressures of responsibility in one way or another make themselves felt. Withdrawal, real or simulated, will probably be a major problem with us for a long time.

The countervailing factor to withdrawal is the possibility of cooperation which modern technological society offers and indeed has to a great extent implemented. We fail all too often to be aware of the fantastic cooperative ventures that the human race has by this time achieved, despite the dissensions that still tear at the national and international fabrics. Man is a cooperating animal, and the earliest human traces on earth show the results of joint action. By the time of the Old Empire in Egypt, shortly after 3000 B.C., cooperative endeavor (not all of it voluntary, but any means) could raise the pyramids. The organization evident in such early works is overwhelmingly impressive, given the conditions of communication and transport under which it was achieved. But in intricacy of detail, it is negligible compared to the cooperation required today for airing a single television program, if one considers all of what is really involved in bringing together the persons and equipment as well as the actual operation of the latter: the skills going into the design and manufacture of television apparatus, the intricacies of program planning, the transportation systems needed for moving personnel to and from the studio (carefully engineered automobiles, subways, freeways patroled by helicopter, traffic-light engineering, and so on ad infinitum). And if the cooperative effort in producing a pyramid or even a medieval gothic cathedral is, for all its wonder, small compared to that needed for a single television broadcast, it is infinitesimal compared to that required to launch a rocket to the moon. Massive cooperation is the hallmark of technological society. Even the routine cooperative activity of a single metropolis in the course of one day surpasses all powers of conceptualization. No one can really disengage himself from the cooperative network of modern living, and in point of fact, few ever really want to.

III

Despite incidental problems it has created and heavy burdens it has imposed on man, the knowledge explosion as described thus far here appears unmistakably as a tremendous achievement and boon. Is this all there is to say about it? Hardly. For human life is tragic at its root, and for all the progress we have made, we have in another sense made no progress at all. The heady sense of growing control over the physical world around us, of growing knowledge concerning man himself, his physical and psychological makeup, and the way he fits historically into the cosmos and into his own social structures can in the long run foster an illusion. For with this kind of knowledge we have actually learned no more at all about what man has always really wanted to know.

The basic, ultimate questions concerning either the exterior universe or our interior consciousness still yawn before us. What is the universe *doing?* If the cosmos is a happening, *what* is going on? What is life all about? Where did my consciousness come from, this "I" that I and I alone can utter, which no one else can savor no matter how much I may wish to share it with him? How could this "I," this spark, without which for me the whole universe ceases to be, once not have been and now actually exist? What is the meaning of my life? What value have my actions? *Why* do I want *others* to judge *me*—approvingly of course, but objectively, on my own merits? What is to be the meaning of my death? The growth in knowledge which we have just reviewed does not lead us toward answers at this level.

It does, of course, bring to light a great deal of new material which can be related to such questions. It also eliminates some false assumptions bearing on such questions: matter is not more spiritual as one moves upward from the earth's surface, as Aristotle thought it was. Moreover, our growth in knowledge enables us to articulate psychological and other complexities which earlier man could not formulate very satisfactorily even when he was acutely aware of them. But enrichment and improved articulation of questions only tantalizes us here so long as it fails to move us further toward satisfying answers. Having discovered as much as we have about the intricacies of the universe, we feel more than ever the urgency of knowing what it is about as a whole. Knowing human history as we do, and thus knowing a great deal about how society has got to where it is, aware that in clearly discernible ways social evolution is patterned, it is natural that we want to know where history is heading. Our knowledge of particular details is now so massive that it can of course distract us from these larger questions for a long time. We have no evidence, however, that this knowledge distracts anyone from them for good. When you raise the questions, others know very well what you are talking about although they may not agree with what you say about them or even with how you formulate them.

Everyone thinks of these things, even though he may try to turn the thought off from time to time or almost for good or may become outraged if the questions are openly broached. It is fashionable, or was a few years ago, to say that life is absurd (a variant of the old statement that it is meaningless). Such a statement may be titillating and can certainly be titillatingly presented. But it accomplishes little. We have not the slightest indication that those who utter or receive it either with composed acquiescence or with starry-eyed excitement cease at all to wonder just the same as before. If they did, the cult of absurdity would not have the shock value it lives on, if it is still alive.

Moreover, not only does our growth in knowledge fail to enter into the basic questions of existence, it also fails to make existence more radically satisfactory for the individual than it would be otherwise. Corporately, knowledge has advanced, but somehow the advance does not touch the individual at the center of his being. How can it? Each of our lives is fresh and unique, a brand new venture into integrity. Knowledge, no matter how much of it is available or how much structure the past experience of man has given it, still has somehow to be built by the individual self into the pattern of a new and induplicable consciousness.

The task can be crushing. Disabilities that most grossly interfere with the individual's functioning as a human being can be ameliorated, and in this sense life can be made more satisfactory: we can realistically hope to eradicate malnutrition and to control more effectively fatal or seriously crippling diseases, or perhaps even inhuman patterns of urban overcrowding, unemployment, and education or lack of education—although we have not been brilliantly successful here. But when all this is done and man's physical needs are filled and his intellectual environment made more habitable, he is still liable to interior collapse. Environment is mostly people, real or imagined. Pressures less visible and tangible but more real than those that may afflict the individual's body can bear in on his mind.

Adequate diet and housing and access to all the sensual and intellectual pleasures that can be dreamed up will not eliminate suicide. And although psychiatry can be of some help, its practitioners certainly do not look forward to an imminent or even an ultimate state of universal well-being. Life is not that way. The psychiatrist can only help man to live with the difficulties that are part of all men's lot. Typically, he spends far more time getting a patient to acknowledge the permanent existence of difficulties than he does in abolishing them.

Our inability to handle our social problems better is due in part, although not entirely, to the problems of the individual. We will always have social problems because whatever else we can do and must do, we have no way of eliminating all individual collapse.

Finally, apart from its limited range and effectiveness, our growth in knowledge holds in its very self threat as well as promise. Most knowledge can be misused, and the power it gives can certainly be misused. There is a touch of death in what man learns. Not a few of the great inventions most useful for peaceful purposes—explosive powder, rocketry, and atom power among them—have been first developed and used to kill other men.

For all these reasons, man's growth in knowledge is both

challenging and tragic. Despite all his progress, man remains a permanent threat to himself, "a being darkly wise and rudely great."

He can and does thrive under such conditions because he is also a being who hopes. As in the past, so today hope concerning the human condition belongs to men not quite settled in the material world immediately around them, much though they may love it, men who sense material reality as something pointing, however darkly, outside itself, an essential intimation of otherness, a something suggesting something it is not. For the fact is that out of his contact with the world around him this question constantly arises in man's mind: Is there something more than this immediacy? And beyond this the further question: Why does this question itself arise, why does man ask whether there is not something more?

In the Hebreo-Christian tradition, this intimation of something more than immediate, sensible reality is subsumed in faith in a personal God, a God who is concerned, to whom men matter. Such faith connects with experience of things, but it relates most directly to man's experience of persons. Man's relationship to God belongs primarily in the realm of personal relationships. It is of a piece with the world in which man speaks to man, heart to heart, in which the mysterious words "I" and "you" are uttered, the world that eludes science but in which all science rests, since it is only a person, an "I," who knows, who can learn, and who can communicate what he learns to others. All science exists in the consciousness of always unique persons, whom science can never get at, for only I know what it feels like to be me, and only you know what it feels like to be you, and what has science to say when death attacks this relationship in which I know you and you know me? Out of what Martin Buber has well styled the primary word of relationship, of binding together, "I-thou," there arises faith as this is known in the Hebrew and Christian heritage.

This personal relationship is not an isolating relationship, since it comes into being in the human community, where the individual discovers his own being, and also in the related community of the faithful. The community of the faithful among the Hebrews constituted the Chosen People. Among Christians the community of the faithful, the Church, is called the People of God—an ancient concept today disseminated by the Second Vatican Council as perhaps never before. The communal grounding of the faith of the People of God further emphasized the personal character of this faith, for community is a relationship between persons, not things.

Like other personal relationships, this faith is of itself abiding. Through it men cling to a personal God in the face of the worst conceivable disasters, like Job, who resisted the attempts of his friends to rationalize the miseries of his life as nothing more than equitable punishments from God's hand. Job knew better. All explanation of evil proved only partial explanation. Finally Job declared his faith in divine providence in the face of what he knew he would always have to live with—his own inability completely to comprehend God's intent and what in fact the full pattern of existence comes to. Despite this inability to comprehend—or indeed because of it, insofar as it showed Job's creaturely status before God —Job believed in God and trusted God fully, leaving himself in God's hands with hope. Job comes to this conclusion not because of reason, or any new explanation he has received or devised, but neither because he feels God is acting against reason. He comes to the conclusion, "I disown what I have said and repent in dust and ashes" (Job 42:6), because God has raised him to a new experience, a new grasp of reality through an encounter with Himself. The solution is a matter not of a scientific or philosophical formula but of Job's own personal relationship to God. He hopes not in any principle of total understanding but simply in God.

Despite the great advance in knowledge and the great

promise further advance holds for the future, there will always be room for this kind of faith, for knowledge is clearly not moving at all in any direction that would engage the problems of existence that faith meets head-on. The Christian's faith partakes of Job's but moves even further into greater hope, for the Christian's faith tells him that God has brought man into personal partnership with himself through the Incarnation, by taking to Himself human nature, entering into this historical, material world in Jesus Christ. This same faith of course is not remote from the growth of knowledge but rejoices in this growth. First, this growth is a good in itself, and faith rejoices in natural good. Secondly, faith can indefinitely deepen its own understanding of itself, and since the man of faith is rooted in the natural, secular world, faith stands to gain by every advance in secular understanding.

One might argue of course, as some do, that Christian faith solves the problem of man's destiny all too well. It eliminates all tragedy, we are told, and with tragedy some of the greatest of man's literary and artistic creations. Does it not make suffering and disaster unreal, or try to, by presenting both as simply preludes to eternal happiness? Even the worst disaster is dissolved in ultimate bliss. The cross is eliminated by the Resurrection.

All students of faith and tragedy do not by any means acquiesce in such an interpretation. To many, including the present writer, such an interpretation badly misses the point of suffering as seen in Christian teaching. Tragedy is tragedy and has to be lived through, by the Christian as by others. Man's relationship to nature is in the last analysis tragic. For it ends always in death.

Million-fuelèd, ' nature's bonfire burns on.
But quench her bonniest, dearest to her, her clearest-selvèd
    spark

Man, how fast his firedint, ' his mark on mind, is gone!
Both are in an unfathomable, all is in an enormous dark
Drowned.

The Jesuit poet Gerard Manley Hopkins has no illusions
about death's absoluteness here in "That Nature Is a Heracli-
tean Fire." Nature ultimately wipes out the individual:

> Manshape, that shone
> Sheer off, disseveral, a star, ' death blots black out; nor mark
> Is any of him at all so stark
> But vastness blurs and time ' beats level.

With Christ, too, suffering and death were real. His
death interrupted his ongoing work, the momentum of his
entire mission. He did not plan his death. It was something
he underwent, a *passio* or passion, not an action, something
that happened to him, not anything he contrived. In Hopkins'
words again, in his letter of July 3, 1886, to R. W. Dixon,
Christ's "career was cut short and, whereas he would have
wished to succeed by success . . . he was doomed to succeed
by failure; his plans were baffled, his hopes dashed, and his
work was done by being broken off undone. However much
he understood all this he found it an intolerable grief to
submit to it. He left the example: it is very strengthening,
but except in that sense it is not consoling." It was Christ's
personal acceptance, his reaction to tragedy, which cost
dearly but was founded on his personal love for his Father
that raised (did not eliminate) tragedy itself to a loftier
action of self-offering and through this brought redemption.

The Christian view of man's career on earth thus ends
in a mystery for contemplation, not in a neat diagram an-
nihilating either evil or the problem of man himself. It is
a view that proposes enlarged perspectives, not narrowed
exclusiveness, truly Catholic in the root sense of this term,
"through-the-whole," a view that on the one hand does not

carry the eye through all the mists but on the other hand is not at all a tentative view but a committed one. Faith makes demands. Christians are called on to die for their faith rather than deny it, and their typical heroes are those who have done so, the "witnesses" or martyrs.

Still, this commitment to something beyond does not in the least exonerate the Christian from the common obligation of all men to do something about the here and now and the future of man on earth. The Christian is committed to this world, or should be, for all the reasons that the complete secularist can urge—the alleviation of suffering, the improvement of living conditions, the promotion of world peace, the general improvement of mankind, and the advance of knowledge not only insofar as it is power but also simply because knowledge is eminently human and a good in itself. Besides these reasons, the Christian can also propose to himself a further and particularly Christian one for advancing the natural, secular world and man's role in it, a reason deriving from his faith: in Christian teaching, not only did God create this world, but he also became incarnate in it, both giving himself to it and taking it to himself in the human nature of Jesus Christ, sharing its miseries and its glory. The Incarnation enhances the worth of the natural and indeed transvaluates it by giving it even a divine significance through adoption. Thus the particular motivation of the Christian as a Christian in his commitment to the natural world is not simply a powerful, or even the most powerful, motivation among others on the same footing but rather a motivation of a transcendent sort, which sees the natural values of the universe in all their integrity caught up into something beyond themselves. Insofar as a Christian does not opt for a program of secular improvement, he is derelict in a particularly desperate way.

The history of benevolent and charitable social organizations among Christians shows a general awareness of commitment to this world even when lack of understanding of natural forces and of control over them has encouraged a psychology of withdrawal. But today we are more than ever intensely aware of Christian secular commitment. Our age has seen a tremendous growth in Christian theology of the secular world, and it has become more and more commonplace that secularization has Hebrew and, even more, Christian roots, if we understand by secularization the tendency to give the secular world an intrinsic value of its own (although not necessarily an ultimate value), as contrasted with secularism, which can refer to the belief that the this-worldly is all there is. The historical fact is that modern secularization, like the science and technology that go with it, in all the 500,000-year history of mankind across the surface of the globe had really only one effective starting point in time and space: a culture of the sixteenth and seventeenth centuries which had lived through a massive experience of Christian teaching. The roots of knowledge run everywhere through all human cultures, but the beginnings of modern science are clearly identifiable.

Back of this culture lay the world of medieval Europe in which universities in the present-day sense of the word began and to which, in one way or another, all universities in the world today trace some of their roots. In his *Science and the Modern World* Alfred North Whitehead has made the point that the extraordinary patience needed to attack a problem scientifically demands faith in the intelligibility of the universe and that historically the great impetus to this act of faith has been the Hebreo-Christian teaching that God made everything, that he is actually concerned about everything in its least detail, and that he is all-wise, the clear implication being that, however hard the answer may be to find, there is always an answer to any question that is properly put and thus that infinite patience and labor in research and reflection are ultimately worthwhile no matter how difficult the matter in hand may be. For all their rationality, even the ancient Greeks had not been so strongly convinced of universal intelligibility. They were haunted by the suspicion that here and there the world was or might be terrifying chaos. This idea of universal intelligibility became widely compelling in twelfth-century and thirteenth-century Europe, when at Paris, Bologna, Salamanca, Oxford, Cambridge, and elsewhere the first universities were taking form and the scholastic thinkers there were developing the scrupulous attention to logical detail characteristic of the modern mind.

It is conventional to state that the first universities matured the distinction between faith and reason which gave the natural, secular world its own intellectual autonomy. But this distinction must not be taken to be more absolute than it actually was. Even with the distinction, reason and faith interacted. Reason was not simply established within a realm in which its own processes ruled but, if Whitehead is right, was also actually strengthened within its own realm by faith, which conveyed its own assurance that reason was worthwhile. Moreover, if reason was indebted to faith for this encouragement, faith itself was helpless without reason, for it needed reason to explicate its own interior organization.

The feeling for knowledge to which universities today are heirs thus traces to complex noetic structures in the past. In these structures the two intellectual worlds, that in which man comprehends and controls nature and that in which he faces his ultimate concerns, were allied at the very time that they were distinct. The alliance and the distinction between the two persist today. Secular knowledge and faith are still related in ways both uneasy and telling. In the midst of our present knowledge explosions, it will take effort to keep alive a fruitful relationship between the two intellectual worlds. But if knowledge is to be advanced—which is virtually the same as saying, if man is to survive—we have to maintain a firm, if inevitably precarious, hold on both.

2

THE FUTURE OF
UNIVERSITY EDUCATION AS AN IDEA

CHARLES MUSCATINE
University of California, Berkeley

IF THE effect of knowledge is to be read in our formal
institutions, the picture of our education in the future
will be close to that of our future itself. "Education of
many different kinds," said scientist Roger Revelle recently
to a congressional committee, "will become the central activity of the people of the United States." Management
professor Warren G. Bennis calls education "the most distinctive characteristic of our society." Sociologists have
named ours a "post-industrial" era, meaning an era in which
the manager moves over to make room for the scholar. "The
university's invisible product, knowledge," writes Clark Kerr,
"may be the most powerful single element in our culture."[1]
In this context, "university education" implies activities of
such scope and importance as to threaten the very identity
of the university. To anyone but the most uncritical booster,

[1] Roger Revelle, "Science and Social Change," presented to the
House Committee on Science and Astronautics, Jan. 26, 1966; Warren
G. Bennis, "The Coming Death of Bureaucracy," *Think*, 32, No. 6
(Nov.–Dec., 1966), 34; Daniel Bell, *The Reforming of General Edu-
cation* (New York: Columbia University Press, 1966), p. 86; Clark
Kerr, *The Uses of the University* (Cambridge, Mass.: Harvard Uni-
versity Press, 1964), p. vi.

in fact, the prospects for university education, while fascinating, are not uniformly hopeful.

It has already become conventional for university people to worry over their future in terms of resources. The population projections and the steady rise in our educational norms are impressive enough: by the year 2000 we may expect between 55 and 71 percent of our college-age youths, that is, between thirteen and sixteen million of them, to be enrolled as "undergraduates" in our "colleges," with another two million in "graduate schools" to boot.[2] I use the quotation marks expecting that the structure of the university will have changed a good deal in the interval. (The extreme alternative—that universities remain essentially the same but just get bigger and more numerous—is almost too awful to contemplate and stands outside our calculations.) Even if we assume—by analogy with what has happened with universal high school education—that in the future many more millions of healthy, active American youths will be able to be safely detained within the classrooms of more and bigger conventional "colleges," some will have found access to more modern institutions, consciously redesigned to meet problems that are obvious today.

In fact, as the demand for university education grows, downright repressive measures may be required to keep higher education from drastic change. For the very alteration of the scale of education will bring problems that even the doubling and redoubling of conventional resources will never answer. The bigger campus will tend to generate and have to fight impersonality, but it will also generate cosmopolitanism and sophistication. It will justify more complex equipment in laboratories and theaters and enjoy a greater variety of talents in faculty and students. More innovative still

---

[2] Alan M. Cartter and Robert Farrell, "Higher Education in the Last Third of the Century," *Educational Record*, 46 (spring, 1965), 119–28.

will be the students' wider social base and range of ideology. On a small campus the rare student with deviant attitudes is cowed or ostracized; on a big campus he joins a club or a movement. The "new generation of students," with its rich mixture of innovative social, political, and moral propensities, can be expected to flourish as college populations rise.

Along with the numbers of students, the mighty expansion of knowledge will transform university education. With an increase in the "graduate" orientation of students, "post-doctoral" studies, refresher courses, and "continuing education" for the sciences and learned professions, the "learning period" will lengthen and the student community will stretch indefinitely through the higher-age groups. The increase in the general maturity of "students" should force the abandonment of much of the disciplinary hardware designed in the nineteenth century for youthful Protestant seminarians and naïve frontier mechanics. There will, indeed, be no time to waste on the ordinary sticks and carrots, on routine quizzing and grading; but better understanding of how people learn will be applied directly, with as little nonsense as possible.

It seems inevitable that the near future will alter the roles of university student and teacher; in this case economy, learning theory, and the rate of obsolescence of knowledge may all three be pushing in the same direction. There will be less routine classroom lecture-and-recitation, because in the first place the faculty will have less time for it. The trend toward dividing the professor's teaching time with research and public service will continue as long as research and public service remain socially and professionally justifiable and as long as well-compensated scholars and scientists, in demand elsewhere, can resist the naked fiats of university administrators and reformers.

When the professor enters the classroom it will be on new terms, largely dictated by his own intellectual situation. In many fields a major force will be the threat of obsolescence, which will make it imperative for the professor to remain abreast of current research, to keep his teaching in close contact with examples of research, and in so doing to emphasize the learning of principles rather than facts. This will mean the abandonment of the "survey" approach in many introductory studies, in favor of the "problems" approach— to teach a method, a stance, a conceptual grasp of a discipline that will be useful long after all the current information is out of date. This approach, by and large, calls for discussion, experimentation, emulation, and the cultivation of personal discovery, rather than for formal indoctrination; it suggests an expanded role of the teacher as guide, explicator, counselor, and critic rather than as formal lecturer. Some of the time for this highly expensive kind of teaching activity will be bought by canceling many of the unnecessary informational courses that are now routinely offered, along with a good deal of the tedious numbers game of grading and credit keeping that goes with them. We are discovering that "contact hours" does not equal education.

But there will never be enough professors to go around, and the university will have to augment its teaching power from other sources. New technology may be of some help, especially with the irreducible busy work and with whatever rote learning and drill work survive in the curriculum. But the major new teaching assistance will come from the students themselves, in the form of discussion groups, seminars led by the more experienced, and a great deal of independent study. Current experiments in this direction are prompted by the hypothesis that the deepest kinds of learning require less constant presence of the teacher than we have hitherto imagined.

Another major new source of university teaching power will be the surrounding community of scientists, technicians, artists, and cultivated people of all sorts. Many can be brought in on a part-time basis to exchange their professional knowledge for the pleasure of teaching. Furthermore, if the university is forced to concentrate on teaching general principles, the up-to-the-minute professional details will have to be left to institutes and training centers close to industry, government, and the professions.

In all this we can already see a profound change in the structure of the university, or rather, a blurring of the notion of the university as a definable structure at all. Here even the "multiversity," with its multiplicity of loci and functions, begins to lose its outlines. As nearly everyone heads for a university education; as the learning period lengthens indefinitely; as the shifting student community expands to include new classes, new age levels, new ranges of ideology; as the procedures of teaching lose their current simplicity and the criteria of learning become more subjective and indefinite; as the conception of who *may* teach includes more and more of those who *can* teach; as professional teachers become more implicated in the worlds of business and government; as more and more "university" instruction goes on in extramural institutions and in field studies here and abroad—the university will tend to lose its character as a place with clear geographical and intellectual boundaries, a place where one spends a definite amount of time and acquires a certain amount of knowledge. It will become, rather, a point or center from which knowledge and teaching radiate into the surrounding environment, and the possible relations of individuals to it will have many gradations, altering with age and circumstances. Some of our current problems of determining just who is to be officially considered a "student" are early symptoms of this condition, as are the growing student taste for off-campus living and other signs of the disintegration of the traditional university community.

However unrealistic this picture may seem in specific detail, it is a plausible one in its outlines, given what we can expect of the future role of knowledge in our culture. If anything, the picture may be a sentimental one. If it predicts more change in a few decades than the university has managed in centuries, it may still be predicting the survival of too much university. In an environment that promises to be almost totally compact of knowledge, the edges of educational institutions will naturally tend to become invisible. Indeed, we might well ask whether there is any reason other than a sentimental one not to expect and not to accept the university's gradual assimilation into the knowledge-producing and knowledge-consuming environment, finally to become indistinguishable in a web of other activity centers of similar purpose.

Resistance to change in the university has indeed a large sentimental component, as well as a large component of insecurity. For some university people the promised uncertainties and ambiguities of the future are simply intolerable; their passionate clinging to the old ways is a clinging to the most comforting symbols of the university's identity. Others are less sentimental than skeptical: in changing so much, they feel, we will not be able to preserve for the university its proper role as conservator and propagator of values of the past. But it would repay these loyal defenders of the university to scrutinize proposed innovations carefully before opposing them. The kinds of changes I have described above are actually a very mixed bag. If most of them threaten to blur the university's physical and intellectual boundaries, at least some of them, if vigorously used, promise a countervailing rehabilitation of the university as a moral force. The fostering of individual responsibility for learning, studies in the field and by one's self, the cultivation of dialogue and debate over real problems—this kind of innovation makes for independence of spirit and for critical thinking. In the coming environment they may well prove to be more valuable symbols of the university idea than any number of cherished traditions. For this we have as witness yet another class of opponents of innovation who (usually beneath appeals to "quality" and to "discipline") actually fear that innovation may embarrass the university with too much moral force altogether.

There are, in short, profound political reasons for preserving the identity of the university, though paradoxically, we shall have to change that identity greatly in order to be able to preserve it at all. To meet the issue more crudely and immediately we need only turn from the problem of knowledge-as-environment to the related problem of knowledge-as-power. Here we have to face it: most educational development today is propelled by the new economic and political potentialities of knowledge, particularly of scientific knowledge. What are the chances that the university will not in one way or another lose its autonomy and identity in the general competition for economic and political power?

Whatever the answer may be, it is mixed with several difficult paradoxes. For millennia we have dreamt of the ideal of the philosopher-prince, or at least of the philosopher at the elbow of the prince. Now its fulfillment seems at hand; but as the scholar flies off to Washington, we wonder where scholarship leaves off and political ambition begins. I refrain from adding to the rich literature on "University Research and the Federal Government." The paradoxes and the dangers are obvious enough.[3] For the whole century of our land-grant universities we have accepted the idea of some sort of collaboration between scholarship and industry. This collaboration has latterly become exceedingly fruitful and close—so close, in fact, that we can now begin to discuss "The Corporation as a College." A recent General

[3] One of the best treatments I have seen is Gerard Piel, "Federal Funds and Science Education," *Bulletin of the Atomic Scientists*, 22, No. 5 (May, 1966), 10–15. On pp. 13–14 Piel cites testimony that in engineering even teaching follows closely the patterns set by defense-supported and space-supported research.

Motors advertisement boasts of an employee, who, "passing up scholarships at two universities, . . . decided instead on the General Motors Institute in Flint, and was graduated with an engineering degree." A Yale economics professor describing "the new corporate curriculum" suggests that it could range from elementary English composition to "courses more advanced than those available in the universities."[4]

As I have suggested above, the universities will need some help from government and industry; what is unpleasant is the prospect that they will receive all too much help, and that in the process "university education" will lose the only subject that has to be taught in a university and that will never appear in the "corporate curriculum," namely, Criticism. By Criticism I mean informed and unconstrained evaluation, the skill that in a democracy we hope every citizen will learn to exercise.

In naming Criticism—in its broadest sense—as the characterizing activity of the university, I am of course invoking an old *idea* of the university that seems lately to be losing ground. It is losing ground to the notion, profoundly typical of our times, that we don't need an idea of a university if we have a description of one. As the Foreword to Clark Kerr's *The Uses of the University* puts it: ". . . in the discussion that follows, analysis should not be confused with approval or description with defense." Nevertheless, the normative idea of the university has its proponents. It is what Gerard Piel has in mind when he says that the university has an obligation to the citizen that is prior to its obligation to the government: "For the university is the seat of the citizen's sovereignty; it is the institutional embodiment of the immunity that hedges his liberty."[5] It is this idea that informs the thinking of those who look to the university as the

---

[4] See *Commentary*, 42, No. 6 (Dec., 1966), p. 62, for the ad; and Neil Chamberlain in *The Atlantic*, 215, No. 6 (June, 1965), 102–4.
[5] On p. 11 of the article cited above.

last source of responsible guidance amid the breakup of the old authorities. It is held perforce by those who, not trusting naked intelligence, are looking for a place that will teach how knowledge can be developed with moral sensitivity.[6]

The university has never anywhere fully exemplified this idea, but we need the idea nonetheless. Whether we shall have even an imperfect but working model of it in the future remains to be seen. We have glanced darkly at forces of disintegration within and without the university and have observed some elements of curricular and organizational change that might make for integrity. What other defenses does our idea of the university have? What, for instance, can be expected of the great university disciplines: natural science, social science, and the humanities?

Too much has been written recently of weakness and venality among our scientific entrepreneurs; it would be fairer to give the scientists another generation in which to become accustomed to their new social status and to ask whether there are forces within the scientific discipline itself that will tend to generate and preserve the critical spirit. The answer, on paper, is yes. If the sciences deal with intrinsically unmoral data, they can deal with them in ways that would seem to have profound moral implications—with skepticism and creative insight, critical detachment, rationality, the demand for verification, the recognition of the tentativeness of knowledge. To the extent that we still have some good science teaching, its qualities will rub off on some students and must be counted among the forces that will preserve the university idea. Looking at science education as an enterprise, we see that the scientists have not gone much beyond this fortuitous rubbing-off. They have

[6] See, among others, Kenneth B. Clark, "Intelligence, the University, and Society," in *The American Scholar*, 36, No. 1 (winter, 1966–67), 23–32; John William Ward, "The Trouble with Higher Education," in *The Public Interest* (summer, 1966), pp. 76–88; J. H. Plumb in *The Saturday Review*, Nov. 26, 1966, pp. 29, 57.

been teaching physics and chemistry and genetics proper, that is, as science, and they have been teaching them better and better to prospective scientists. But with pitifully few exceptions criticism of science stops at the borders of the technical field. In this, science teachers have been widely short-changing the prospective nonscientists, whose appreciation of science depends on seeing it in the context of their culture, its history, and its values.

Perhaps we should not ask too much of the natural scientists in these boom times. Success and excitement are not the best conditions for philosophical self-examination. Besides, Criticism in the social and moral realms is not the natural scientist's professional forte. But can we say the same of the social scientist and the humanist? We may readily observe that detachment, impersonality, and rigorous scientific objectivity, when they are practiced as ends in themselves and to the exclusion of all else, can render a man and his work morally sterile. This may not affect the gross production of knowledge, but for the idea of the university it is crucial. The most serious betrayal of this idea today is the moral anesthetization of the social sciences and humanities which generally goes on in the name of "science," "research," and "objective scholarship."

About the full condition of the social sciences I cannot pretend to much authority. I know enough of the relative decline of political theory and economic history and of the vogue of "mathematical" economics and politics to make me worry. Most of all, I am concerned that so very few of the social scientists I know of are saying (or have ever said) anything so unsettling about society as to require protection by the academic freedom and tenure that society has generously vouchsafed them.

With the humanities I am in more familiar territory. Where else should Criticism flourish but in the humanities? Of criticism with a small c we have plenty—this is an "age of criticism"—but of studies informed with large moral vision we have little. The case of philosophy is typical. Metaphysics and idealism are nearly dead, trampled in the rise of "scientific philosophy," now largely concerned with the critical analysis of logic and language. One hears that this tool sharpening is just a phase, prelude perhaps to a grand new attempt to grasp this sorry scheme of things entire. We can only hope so.

The teaching of literature is in slightly better case, if only because literature's academic establishment is a formidable one, including many of our creative writers. Even so, the teaching of non-Western literature is generally neglected, and the established departments of the European literatures are widely suffering for lack of fresh talent. Let us concentrate on English, a prospering field marked by continually impressive feats of scholarship and criticism.

As Professor John Gerber has recently made clear in a witty and plausible historical sketch,[7] for the last century the trend in literary studies in America has ever been toward detachment. The revolt from factualism loudly heralded by the New Criticism thirty years ago did not turn teacher and student back to the emotional appeal and moral relevance of literature but rather substituted the detachment of critical analysis for that of Germanic scholarship. The New Criticism's corrective for studying matters extraneous (and often irrelevant) to the work of literature was to concentrate attention on the work *in itself*. This has yielded us splendid results in the techniques of close reading and in the appreciation of formal structure. But the effort to eliminate historical irrelevance and personal idiosyncrasy from literary interpretation has ended up in a kind of estheticism that is frequently just as far from commitment to human values as is the production of the chemist and of the logician. What

[7] "Literature—Our Untamable Discipline," *College English*, 28 (Feb., 1967), 351–58.

literary studies need now is in the first place a New Historicism that will put its elegantly analyzed artifacts back into the living stream of the history of culture. In the second place, those of us who profess to teach literature need to accept the special role that comes with the territory. Handling stuff that is itself alive with feeling and with moral significance, we cannot afford to be always detached.

As professionals it is we who have the most direct responsibility to keep Criticism alive in the university. Our relative failure is partly the result of a long and misguided attempt to make literature into a discrete science. We have resisted our natural role as humanists and generalists, for fear that in the competitive university environment we would be thought to be lacking a professional "field."[8] The same fear has now infected even the secondary school teaching of literature. Competing with "new science" and "new math," and propelled by the reaction against progressivism—which is now resulting in uncritical hostility to the cultivation of sensibility in any form—high school curricula are filling up with professional Literary History and Critical Analysis of Texts at the expense of the education of judgment and feeling that should be their prior aim.

The recent creation of a National Endowment for the Humanities may ultimately help transform the stance of our academic humanists. At least it gives them the kind of recognition that may free them to be their best selves. At the same time we must recognize that the Endowment and the National Council for the Arts and Humanities under which it is organized have been created under the impetus of men who speak largely from the old, well-upholstered

---

[8] *Cf.* the whole drift of R. Wellek and A. Warren, *Theory of Literature* (New York: Harcourt, Brace & World, 1962); and the excellent remarks of Richard Ohmann, "The Size and Structure of an Academic Field: Some Perplexities," *College English*, 28 (Feb., 1967), 359–67.

positions.[9] Early reports of the Humanities Endowment projects seem largely to favor conventional scholarship. We can freely grant that support of scholarship is essential: it provides us some of the major materials of Criticism. But it is not enough. We have nothing to indicate that more direct contribution to human values will result except the rather grand but cloudy pronouncements of the humanities establishment. If, as we hope, humanistic study makes people more humane and sensitive to human problems, we should perhaps be bolder in looking among those who show conspicuous effects of such study when we award humanities fellowships and recruit humanities professors.

But, as the *Bulletin of the Atomic Scientists* regularly testifies, men are not humanists exclusively by profession; the university community can practice Criticism without regard to the branches of learning. (In this respect the scientists—particularly the physicists and mathematicians—come off well in proportion to their numbers.) Professors have led public debate on the issues of technology and public welfare, and they are conspicuous in the groups currently debating the morality of American domestic and foreign policy. But the numbers engaged on either side of such issues are small, and the generally beleaguered tone of critical faculty groups indicates how far even these men feel from their normal calling. Some of their diffidence and their vulnerability comes from trying to fill the moral vacuum left in the curriculum by others. Mathematicians do not feel comfortable doing the

[9] See, *e.g.*, Howard Mumford Jones, *One Great Society: Humane Learning in the United States* (New York: 1959); and the *Report of the Commission on the Humanities*, American Council of Learned Societies (New York, 1964). An exception is Henry Allen Moe, briefly chairman of the National Endowment, who said to the ACLS at its 1966 annual meeting that "the curse of humanistic scholarship in my time has been pedantry." *Cf.*, in agreement, Eric Larrabee, "Saving the Humanities," *Commentary*, 42 (Dec., 1966), 53–60; and William Arrowsmith, "The Future of Teaching," in *Improving College Teaching*, C. B. T. Lee, ed. (Washington, 1967), pp. 57–71.

work of political scientists, and physicists are unhappy substituting for historians. But mostly the uneasiness is recognition of their estrangement from the majority of the faculty itself. The majority simply do not feel it their proper business to become "involved."

The trouble is not merely an excess of scholarly detachment; our universities are overrun with men who have no roots in the university tradition of critical thought at all. They are most of them, ironically, our own alumni, graduated as technicians from our own technical curricula (and I do not except history, philosophy, and literature). They have about the same attitude toward the university as do those other, nonacademic, alumni from Yale to Berkeley who see nothing wrong with academic freedom until someone exercises it. For generations, too, our administrators have been "selling" the university to alumni and general public alike. They have sold it simply as an economic advantage to the graduate and the community and have been content to appeal to alumni loyalty on the most puerile level. This easy salesmanship becomes a terrible liability when the issue is the preservation of the university as a source of Criticism.

The future of *university* education, as opposed to the standard product of the knowledge factory, depends less on specific curricular innovations than on a reform of the stance of men. In their present attitudes, today's faculty, administrators, and alumni do not promise more than feeble resistance to the tides of power and interest rising on all sides. There is more hope in some of our students, who have lately become the truest spokesmen we have for the university idea. The student movement has its unattractive elements; it has its share of intolerance, tastelessness, and sheer hostility. Yet beneath the special political motives, beneath the posturing and slogan making of some student leaders, there is a strong current of genuine thought and feeling for the welfare of the university. Students across the nation have already shown by their general unrest that something is terribly wrong with university education today. Thus far they have not been conspicuous in presenting constructive changes. But their specific complaints are instructive enough: their demands for relevance, involvement, moral guidance, and social responsibility point to just those defects in the curriculum and in the personal conduct of university men which have been mentioned above. To these they add defects of personal warmth and of human sympathy. Of course they are asking the university to make up some of the defects of the society as a whole, and there is no reason why they should not. If the traditional sources of sympathy and of moral exercise—the family, the church, the community—seem to be failing in influence, the university as yet does not. With its growth, its prestige, its still lofty affirmations of purpose, it remains a likely resort for student idealism.

Where this fierce idealism comes from is something of a mystery, but we should be thankful for it. There is little of it in the educational system itself. Yet, one hopes that what little there is has had its effect. It is as if for years we had taught Freedom, Democracy, the need for Criticism—for years had been assigning Plato, Voltaire, Jefferson, Thoreau, Emerson, Mill—and suddenly there appeared a generation of students with the temerity to take it all literally! Either that, or through some collective instinct for survival the young have received from their environment the message that their future as free men is bound up with that of the idea of the university itself.

What I have been calling the idea of the university has not always in the past been *in* the university. For much of its history, in fact, the university has no more been a stronghold of Criticism than it has been at the forefront of new learning. It would be fatuous of us to imagine that without the university as we know it, freedom of opinion in our society would perish. The few "free universities" that have recently sprung up outside the walls are limited by their biases and by their lack of resources, but they will do to illustrate that the established institution is never the last resort. Yet the established institution, the university, *is* now at the forefront of learning, and it would be a great pity if it were not also to become the great critical agency in our society. For freedom of opinion is valuable in proportion as the opinion is informed. Somewhere beneath the newly appreciated idea of knowledge-as-power, the American faith in education still draws strength from the notion of knowledge-as-virtue, that somehow if a man knows more he has a better chance to be wise. Either the university of the future will take hold of the connections between knowledge and human values, or it will sink quietly and indistinguishably into the noncommittal moral stupor of the rest of the knowledge industry.

3

THE FUTURE OF LEARNING IN TROPICAL AFRICA*

ERIC ASHBY
University of Cambridge, England

"SALT FROM THE NORTH, gold from the south, and silver from the white man's country; but the word of God and the treasures of wisdom are to be found in Timbuctoo." So runs a Sudanese proverb. Four centuries ago the mosque of Sankoré, near the banks of the Niger, was the center of learning in tropical Africa. It attracted scholars from as far afield as Fez and Cairo. The mosque of Sankoré still stands in Timbuctoo, a squat structure of stones and red-baked earth under a blazing sky; but today it is only an echo of Africa's past. Africans now seek "the treasures of wisdom" in Europe and America, or in African universities that are facsimiles of European or American models. The University of Nsukka displays a striking family likeness to a Midwest land-grant college; Lovanium University in the Congo is a scion of Louvain; Makerere in Uganda is an unmistakably British export. Even the ancient strongholds of Muslim higher education in Fez and Cairo are now westernized. The intellectual life of Africa has been diverted into new channels by three forces: Christianity, trade, and technology. The Brothers of Ploermel in Senegal, the Church

* See p. 66 for Bibliographical Summary to chapter.

Missionary Society in Nigeria, the Basel missionaries in the Gold Coast, brought the Cross to replace the idol; but they brought also writing to replace oral tradition, and hygiene to replace magic. The traders replaced barter by a money economy. And technology has sucked Africa into the contemporary world; today it is the most compelling force of all: the printing press, the automobile, the aeroplane, the transistor radio, and the television set have lifted Africa suddenly into the Broadway of the Western world. Today the tropical African countries stand fascinated by the sudden dazzle and din of technology, at times doubtful and suspicious of it, but certain they cannot now turn back. That Africa will continue to acquire the material equipment of the Western world there is no doubt. The whole range of the white man's civilization, from his high achievements in literature and science to his shameful indulgences in frivolity, reappear in African societies, just as a dominant factor reappears in the breeding of animals and plants. There is something very touching about the African graduate whose eyes light up as he confesses that his research problem is the poetry of Dryden and Pope; or about the delegation of students in Uganda who urged me to persuade Makerere College to introduce the teaching of Latin; or about the tense shining faces of Yoruba children watching an American cowboy film. But this acceptance of the Western intellectual style, this patina of European culture, this social mimicry of a different race—are they firm foundations for an indigenous African civilization in the future (as similar manifestations in American intellectual life a hundred years ago were for an indigenous American civilization)? Or are they too superficial to support anything but a false and alien way of life? In the words of the Haitian poet Leon Laleau (translated by Samuel W. Allen), for the African, Western culture can mean:

> This beleaguered heart
> Alien to my language and my dress

On which bite like a brace
The borrowed sentiments and customs of Europe.

Yet he covets the culture and embraces it eagerly.

It is not sufficient for Western countries to leave Africans to reflect on these problems. Many Western countries are giving massive intellectual aid to Africa—teachers, scholarships, money for buildings and books. They are pumping American or British or French civilization into the forests and savannahs between Cancer and Capricorn. To what end? With what ultimate design? Only the French, I think, have tried to answer these questions. Their answer is to create an élite of black Frenchmen and, among the rest, a sufficient respect for French language and institutions to ensure a stable community in the French style, a policy of cultural imperialism which started at the turn of the century and was consolidated by Albert Sarraut in the 1920s. It has been surprisingly successful. What better testimonial could an imperial power want than this assertion (about the founding of a university in Dakar) made by a Guinean representative at the French Assembly in 1950:

> We want to have higher education at home, but we want it to be exactly equal to that of the Métropole. We want a Metropolitan curriculum . . . and the same diplomas as in France, for we are as French as are the French of the Métropole.

The superficial consequences of this policy are evident; anyone who has crossed the border between western Nigeria and Dahomey notices an astonishing contrast between the imperfect English of the anglophone Yoruba and the elegant French of the francophone Yoruba. But its deeper consequences are less easy to interpret. The most nostalgic movement back to African indigenous culture is *négritude*, expressed in the French language but protesting against the dominance of French culture. And it was a group of French-speaking intellectuals in Leopoldville who published, in *Conscience africaine*, the cry: "We wish to be civilized Congolese, not black-skinned Europeans."

History is on the side of *Conscience africaine*. Even similar races, despite a millennium of traffic between them, develop characteristic and indigenous cultures. The Latin people have been in England since A.D. 43 and are still constantly intermixing with the British. Barely more than a century ago Latin was the common language among scholars from Scotland to Sicily (as late as 1830, examinations for medical degrees in Edinburgh were still being held entirely in Latin). Yet the British and Italians have an utterly different style of life. The North American people are not just Europeans living under central heating; in less than two centuries there has developed something one can call American culture. It would be surprising, therefore, if the countries of tropical Africa remain indefinitely no more than intellectual colonies of one or other of the aid-giving Western nations. But the future of learning in tropical Africa does depend on attitudes and policies in Washington, Paris, and London, as well as on policies in Nairobi, Lagos, and Dakar.

Tropical Africa provides a paradigm of a problem common to all developing countries and to all countries dispensing intellectual aid. The problem can be compressed into a sentence: The countries dispersing aid have shown more generosity than wisdom, and the countries receiving aid have been more concerned with short-term opportunism than long-term consolidation. Hundreds of gifted and dedicated teachers from many nations have brought higher education to the developing countries. They have brought it as the early missionaries brought Christianity to these same countries: in the firm conviction that this—unchanged—was the unique key to prosperity, just as the gospel was the unique key to salvation. And leaders in developing countries have welcomed universities with even more enthusiasm and less criticism than their grandparents displayed toward churches. Indeed, if a handful of enlightened West Africans had had their way there would have been a university on the west coast in the 1860s.

The three forces, Christianity, trade, and technology, all conspired to persuade Africans that their own past was contemptible and useless as a foundation for the future. Therefore their first reaction to the importation of Western learning was a euphoric welcome to it. The early results of accepting it were highly encouraging. From Dakar in Senegal to Dar-es-Salaam in Tanzania, Africans found that they could master Western learning as successfully as Europeans could. The examinations they took allowed no softening of standards and no concession to the deficiencies of their schooling. The degrees awarded to them were from the University of London or were moderated by the universities of Louvain, Bordeaux, or Paris. At the same time, under schemes such as the African Scholarship Program of American Universities (ASPAU), Africans were brought to some of the best American universities, and their academic performance was substantially above the American average! By 1960, when one African country after another was securing independence, Africans had demonstrated to the world their capacity to absorb and digest the intellectual diet offered to the best students in Cambridge, Cornell, or the Sorbonne.

"To absorb and digest" . . . but there is more to the intellectual life than this. Learning has no future in a developing country if it remains just learning; it has to become self-reproducing, inventing its own techniques, propagating its own values, becoming not just a recipient, but a donor, of world knowledge. In a word, there must be indigenous scholarship and research in Africa; and if these are to become anything more than mere outposts of European and American learning, Africans must not only preserve their loyalty to a Western tradition, they must also rediscover and proclaim a loyalty to some indigenous values in African society.

Let us now examine this proposition more closely. The universities in Nigeria, Ghana, Senegal, East Africa, and the Sudan are already lively centers of scholarship. Every one of them produces every year a respectable list of books and articles in learned journals. Some of the research is done by Africans and is on African themes. In certain fields, notably the use, in historical research, of oral tradition and archaeology to supplement the written word, Africans are certainly becoming donors to world knowledge. But something is lacking, not only from scholarship in tropical Africa but from scholarship in countries with a much longer tradition of inherited learning, such as India. What is lacking is the fertile soil of public appreciation, the stimulus of audience participation in the intellectual life of the country. In modern technological jargon, the intellectual life of developing countries lacks feedback.

It is very difficult to pursue learning without feedback. Consider the difficulties that confront a university professor in tropical Africa as he does research in, say, chemistry or history. His audience is the scholarly world of chemists or historians. The nearest colleague in his specialism may be thousands of miles away. His articles will go unread by his countrymen. The very journals in which they are published are edited across the ocean. If he is an expatriate, all his roots are overseas; he may be dedicated to African education, but he draws his sustenance from Oxford or Columbia. If he is an African—and this is the point made so vividly for Indians by Edward Shils in his book *The Intellectual Between Tradition and Modernity*—his family roots are at home but he still has to draw his sustenance from overseas. As an African his loyalty is to his people and his country; as a scholar his loyalty is to the international community of historians or chemists. This dual loyalty is, of course, shared by all scholars; the peculiar difficulty for the scholar in a developing country is that the two loyalties scarcely overlap; for one of them, on which the future of learning depends in his country, the scholar is obliged to look beyond his own people. His only hope of survival as a scholar is to have his intellectual roots in an alien land.

This difficulty is not peculiar to non-European races. Even Australia, even North America in earlier days, were Europe-centered. It would not be an exaggeration to say that although Australia was freed from Britain politically sixty-seven years ago, it was still dependent on Britain intellectually up to World War II. Indeed, as late as 1960, when the University of Sydney celebrated its centenary, about half the nonmedical professors in the university had taken their first degrees out-side Australia. It is only in the last twenty years that Australia has become a distinguished self-sustaining intellectual com-munity.

This, then, is the first difficulty. The future of learning in a developing country depends not only on a small élite of active scholars; they must work in a soil that nourishes them. There must, for example, be an intellectual press, such as *Harper's* and *The New Republic* provide in the United States. There must be listeners as well as speakers at seminars and conferences. There must be reasoned constructive criticism of ideas from within the country. No one familiar with developing countries doubts for a moment that these countries can produce men of the highest intellectual caliber, capable of the most distinguished scholarship. What is missing in the developing countries is the matrix within which these scholars can work fruitfully.

The universities of tropical Africa are the centers from which this matrix can spread to schools, government depart-ments, the press, and publishing houses. It is an essential task of the university in Africa to create the urbane society from which learning can draw its sustenance. Therefore extension work, which plays a greater part in the American state uni-versity than it does in British or French universities, becomes in developing countries an activity absolutely vital for the future of learning. This has not been sufficiently recognized in some of the universities of tropical Africa, with the result that the intellectuals have become dangerously isolated from the people. The taunt of "ivory tower," so commonly leveled at some African universities, is a symptom of this; no one would call a Midwest land-grant college an ivory tower, whatever other weaknesses it might have. Therefore—to come back to the questions asked at the beginning of this essay—let us face the fact that intellectual aid to foster scholarship and research in developing countries is likely to fall on stony ground unless it is accompanied by a massive program of extension work deliberately organized to create an intellectual community; the nation giving aid must prepare the soil as well as transplant the seedling.

But extension work, even if it is rapidly successful, will not by itself assure the future of learning in any developing country. Scholars must have communication with minds as good as or better than their own, as well as with an appreciative audience in their own country. And these superior minds are inevitably abroad. How can aid-giving countries bring the African (or Asian) scholar in contact with his peers? Already there are generous arrangements for faculty members from universities in developing countries to spend study leave in the mainstreams of academic life; there are arrangements, too, for European and American scholars to go on secondment to African and to Asian universities. But this infrequent, spasmodic experience is not enough. Sustained scholarship requires sustained sustenance. Some better solution than the sabbatical year, or the eight-week summer visit to Britain, is needed; and it is the aid-giving countries that ought to find the solution. Already there is one promising experiment, the International Centre for Theoretical Physics in Trieste. A small band of scientists of international repute is always to be found at the institute, and alongside them, financed by grants from international agencies, are workers from developing countries who spend from one to four months a year at the institute. Here is an idea worth very serious thought. If we in the aid-giving countries are to make the most effective contribution to the future of learning in developing countries, could we not encourage, and finance, arrangements that would bring scores of *active* scholars (not scholars who have fallen into administration or scholars who have become perpetually airborne on government missions) for three months a year to international centers (some in existing universities, some on their own as in Trieste), where they will spend full time on research? Each scholar would come to regard his center as his intellectual home. His bench, his table in the library, would be there, awaiting his return year after year; but (an essential part of the contract) he would return to his own country, year after year, to teach and to build up an indigenous school of research and scholarship. Of course universities that allow some of their faculty members to spend three months a year elsewhere will need a richer staff-student ratio than otherwise would be necessary; but this, too, would in the long run be a good investment in overseas aid.

The future of learning in developing countries is at present very hazardous. Aid-giving countries, by redeploying their resources, might greatly reduce the hazard; and the two most promising avenues for redeployment are, one: a massive campaign designed to create, through special kinds of university extension work, self-sustaining intellectual communities; and two, arrangements that would enable the most productive scholars in developing countries to immerse themselves in the mainstream of scholarship for three months of every year.

But what about the assumption that underlies these proposals for the future of learning in developing countries? It is the assumption that the studies appropriate for universities in Manchester, Bordeaux, and St. Louis are *ipso facto* appropriate in Bombay, Tananarive, and Nsukka. In some areas of study the assumption is plainly correct. Science and technology are supranational; the laws of nature and the properties of matter are everywhere the same. Not only the methods of research but its actual content are common to all mankind. But the range of humanistic studies appropriate for an African, an Indian, a Brazilian, and a Japanese are patently not common to all mankind, even though there are common elements in the techniques of scholarship in these humanistic studies. And when one digs below the level of the purely intellectual life, and reaches strata of values, one has to ask whether it is possible for a developing country to enter the stream of Western civilization without adopting the social philosophies of the West. Is technology (for instance) inseparable from a competitive society? If an African accepts an American education and pursues scholarship in the American style, does he inevitably have to adopt the criteria for success common in America, or even to submit himself to an un-African obedience to the clock?

This essay leaves these questions unanswered. Any attempt to answer them would be disingenuous. But the long-term future of learning in developing countries depends on the answers. It is unlikely that any Westerner would now be so arrogantly parochial as to suggest that Buddha and Mahomet can be neglected because of Christ, or the *Mahabharata* rejected in favor of *Paradise Lost*. Even tropical Africa, although it has no written literature, is acknowledged as a rich source of original music and sculpture and folklore, and anthropologists have accumulated a fascinating literature on the religious and cosmological ideas and the social and ethical values that for a thousand years have given coherence and meaning to the lives of Africans. In a remarkable and important book, *The Primal Vision*, John V. Taylor, who was a missionary in Africa, has paid tribute to the indigenous value systems of the pagan African—the placid disregard for the passing of time, the sense of obligation to the extended family, the "tranquillity of human relationships." And he quotes from an account by J. B. Danquah of the qualities expected in an elected chief among the Akan:

> He had married and been given in marriage with honour; he had bought or sold in open or private market with honour; he had been a member of the company of fighting men with honour; he had sowed and reaped with honour; suffered famine or enjoyed plenty with honour; brought up children with honour; worshipped at the shrines with honour; had suffered bereavement with honour; and, above all, had joined with others, or acted by himself, to settle family and other disputes, bringing peace and increase to the family with honour.

It will be a sad day for the future of the humanities in tropical Africa if traditions and values such as this passage describes are buried beneath the trivia of imitative studies of Western literature and philosophy. It is sometimes said that we shall have to leave the Africans themselves to decide what to accept and what to reject from Western tradition, and to blend what they accept with their own traditional cultures. I cannot agree with this view. Those who designed models of Western education for export must be willing to continue to cooperate with Africans in the adaptation of these designs to incorporate African indigenous values. (The same is true, of course, with even greater emphasis, for countries, such as India, which had a splendid literature centuries before Virgil, and a sophisticated philosophy centuries before Plato.) Indeed, the most valuable contribution that scholars from aid-giving countries can make to the future of learning in Africa is to apply the rigorous techniques of Western scholarship to African problems so that there is no doubt about the respectability of these problems for research. And the most valuable contribution that the African professor can make to the future of learning in Africa is—apart from his own research—to ensure that *all* African undergraduates are introduced to the scholarly approach to these problems, so that there grows up in these very fragmented societies, from Niger to the Zambesi, a common core of culture not entirely derived from outside Africa.

Bibliographical Summary

THE main sources of information on African higher education are E. Ashby, assisted by M. Anderson, *Universities, British, Indian, African: A Study in the Ecology of Higher Education* (Cambridge, Mass.: Harvard University Press, 1966), and E. Ashby, *African Universities and Western Tradition* (Cambridge, Mass.: Harvard University Press, 1964).

The difficulties of life as a scholar in a country with no self-sustaining intellectual community are brilliantly analysed by E. Shils, *The Intellectual Between Tradition and Modernity: The Indian Situation*, Comparative Studies in Society and History (The Hague: Mouton, 1961).

The proposal for bringing scholars from developing countries every year into the mainstream of world scholarship springs from the experience of the International Centre for Theoretical Physics in Trieste, described in *Minerva*, 3, 1965, 533–36, by M. J. Moravcsik, "Some Practical Suggestions for the Improvement of Science in Developing Countries," *Minerva*, 4, 1966, 381–90; and by Abdus Salam, "The Isolation of the Scientist in Developing Countries," *Minerva*, 4, 1966, 461–65.

The complexity and sometimes sophistication of African ideas and values and institutions are well described in three collections of articles: *African Worlds*, Daryll Forde, ed. (London: Oxford University Press, 1954); *African Political Systems*, M. Fortes and E. E. Evans-Pritchard, eds. (London: Oxford University Press, 1940); and *Continuity and Change in African Cultures*, W. R. Bascom and M. J. Herskovits, eds. (Chicago: University of Chicago Press, 1959).

A sensitive and beautifully written book, *The Primal*

Vision, by J. V. Taylor (London: Student Christian Movement Press, 1963) is a vivid assertion of the depth of thought and feeling in African society as seen by a Christian missionary. Another equally illuminating book is Adam Curle's *Educational Strategy for Developing Countries* (London: Tavistock Publications, 1963).

4

THE FUTURE OF INTERNATIONAL
POLITICS

HARLAN CLEVELAND

AN INQUIRY INTO the future of international relations
must start with a guess about what kinds of international political communities will be most in evidence, what
issues will be featured in their politics, and who the actors
will be.

The community-building stimuli are predictable; what
cannot be foreseen is the reaction of men and nations to them.
But recent history suggests that when science and technology
make possible a new or extended form of cooperation, national
frontiers are readily set aside and national governments are
pushed by their own interested constituencies to make the
necessary international agreements. The United States, which
went to one international conference a year in the nineteenth
century, attended nearly seven hundred of them in 1966.

As examples, here are some of the developments that will
call into being new international structures or force the
adaptation of existing ones:

• Man will reach the moon and won't stop there. The
farther he gets from Earth, the more irrelevant will seem the
national frontiers, the more necessary and natural an international approach to the exploration of outer space. If evi-

dence is found of another intelligence with which man can communicate, the drawing together of Earth's inhabitants will be all the more rapid.

• Meanwhile, the use of outer space will bring about another revolution in communications and transportation around our little globe. The nearness of nations to one another will force them to think seriously about forms of cooperation which have never before been more than academic.

• Earth satellites, cloud photography, and fast computers will enable man for the first time to watch the whole of the world's weather at once. His forecasts will improve in quality and stretch out farther into time. And he will start *changing* some kinds of weather, in some places, at human command.

• Nations with great arsenals of nuclear and other "sophisticated" weapons systems will contemplate the futility of possessing more than enough destructive power to wipe out whole societies—and turn seriously to designing international controls over the level and deployment of such armaments.

• Ways will have to be found to erode, and in time erase, the division of Berlin, Germany, and Europe. The arrangements will have to be somehow guaranteed internationally by the powers that enter into them.

• Ways will have to be found to regulate the small-power arms races and inhibit the spread of weapons of mass destruction to nations that cannot afford them. Yet small wars will persist, and ways will have to be found, also, to provide armed peacekeepers to prevent conflicts and police cease-fires and agreements. As one near-term example, the war in southeast Asia will have to lead to some form of settlement—and some kind of peacekeeping machinery—by which the conquest of some nations by others can be prevented without the enormous input this now requires from the outside.

• The nation-based ideologies with which we are now familiar will wear out as more and more national leaders adapt social theory and political polemic to the insistent demands of increasingly complex technological societies with increasingly international ramifications.

• The gap between the rich countries and the poor countries will widen. All economies will grow, and many poor economies will prosper in time, but the most developed countries will control a disproportionate share of the total growth. This state of affairs will sooner or later become politically intolerable; pressure from the poor and a sense of missionary obligation among the rich will require a massive transfer of resources. How these resources are transferred, and what mutual obligations their transfer creates, will be a prime object of the politics of the future—though the basic approach of "self-help and mutual aid" will prevail.

• World population will grow, perhaps to six billion by the turn of our century. Most of the growth will be urban and will occur in the developing societies, especially in Asia and Latin America. The growth may not be so explosive as the demographers are now predicting, because the combination of knowledge, chemicals, and women's instincts may be explosive in their own way. But the biggest increases may well come in this next generation, and the international community will somehow have to cope with the resulting economic (food, employment) and social (urban living) problems.

• The penetration of "outsiders" into the internal affairs of nations will grow, not decline. In the "new," "developing" "nations" of Africa and Asia, the atavistic nationalism so characteristic of the post-colonial 1960s is bound to be as shortlived as it is nonfunctional. Outsiders are needed to provide technical aid and military muscle, and sometimes even to furnish convenient political scapegoats for necessary but unpopular decisions by weak governments; but their selection, the regulation of their behavior, especially the control of the political use of their power, will increasingly be regarded as an international problem.

• The social problems of urban growth and congestion,

seriously tackled by no nation so far, will be increasingly regarded as international in scope. The pollution of air and the shortage of clean water; delinquency and the slum fringe; how to reconcile the need for growing productivity with cradle-to-grave security; the creation of city jobs for marginal farm workers; the unwillingness of people to stay at the "village level"—these problems are universal in the urbanizing societies, and all societies are urbanizing.

• Man's capacity to manage large human events will be put to the test as more and more activities can be managed only on a worldwide, or at least intercontinental, scale. In the generation just past, the big discovery was long-range planning by public institutions. We can guess from American experience that in the next generation, the new discovery about large-scale international management will be not "planning" but creative and pluralistic improvisation on a general sense of direction. But that requires an unprecedented sense of freedom in "leaders" that begin to be counted in the millions.

• For this and other reasons, the next stage in the history of freedom is likely to feature, not the rights of ethnic and racial groups, but the rights of individual men, women, and children. The revolutions of national independence and racial equality have led to new opportunities and also to new evidence that man's inhumanity to man does not disappear with colonial rule and enforced discrimination. How the international community organizes to protect individuals against the nations and groups to which they "belong" may prove to be the most explosive of all forms of international politics.

These are but a dozen of a hundred possible examples of trends that will stimulate international organization. In every field of science and technology (including "social" sciences and technologies), breakthroughs are common; more and more intensive forms of international cooperation are therefore commonplace. Biologists have yet to learn what life is, what really goes on inside a cell; psychologists have only begun to observe the mind systematically, let alone explain or predict its behavior. In almost every field of scholarship, the men and women closest to its frontiers are those most impressed with the paucity and the limited relevance of our knowledge so far.

So the only safe assumption for an institution builder is that new scientific discoveries, new theoretical perceptions, and new technologies will continue, at an accelerating rate, to require us to build new international institutions so that the new technologies can work for, and not against, the future of man.

II

A technological imperative thus makes greater international cooperation likely in every department of man's destiny. Some pundits and politicians see the growing need for international actions causing the nation-state to wither away; the requirement for man's survival, they think, will turn out to be some form of world government. But while the writers of ideal constitutions have been writing, the nation-state has been showing—again—an astonishing resilience and adaptability.

In our own time the nation-state has survived the internationalism of world religions, of corporate business, and of Communist ideology. Indeed, the striking thing about all three of these forms of internationalism is that they have had to clothe themselves in national trappings—and bend their doctrines to match—in order to win acceptance.

The "Christian" parties in Europe are reinforcements, not challenges, to the nation-state. The political urge of Islamism, Hinduism, and even Buddhism is increasingly fulfilled by direct participation in national struggles for secular power. Most Christian missionaries, especially in their three hundred Protestant incarnations, have shown a willingness to promote and assist parochial nationalisms which is astonishing in salesmen of supposedly universal values. Priestly endorsement of short-term secular national aims has traditionally come cheap, even from the Universal Church; Cardinal Spellman's pep talk to the Americans fighting in Vietnam, which occasioned some controversy at the time, was merely one incident in a long and distinguished Christian tradition.

Capitalism and communism, while likewise professing a doctrinal universality, also have found that their successes come mainly from operating not against but for, not outside but inside, the framework of national economies and national governments. Communist parties have succeeded in establishing themselves in those few places where, as in Stalin's Russia, they concentrated mostly on building socialism in one country; and have failed where as in western Europe and America and Africa and most of Asia, the national Communist parties could not help looking like agents, or at least stooges, of a foreign *national* power. Big corporations operating across international frontiers have found that the best formula for business success is to stop looking "foreign" and start looking like an indigenous piece of the national landscape.

The success of the nation-state in absorbing its internationalist invaders has led in our time to grotesque caricatures of national sovereignty. Just when the Atlantic peoples were seeking answers to their market and security problems in wider and closer associations of nations, the new young leaders of subject peoples, educated mostly in Western schools, were insisting on national independence and on calling their development efforts "nation building." Once again the political energy generated by the universally valid Greek idea that citizens of a polity should make their own laws rather than receiving them from priestly or royal authority—and the universally valid claims for racial equality and better living standards—were applied within, rather than against, the nation-state.

III

Experience does not therefore enable us to write off the nation-state as a dying object of relevant loyalties or a withering form of political organization. Indeed it suggests that for the rest of this century we will be reckoning with the nation-state as a basic building block in every form of international community.

Yet there *are* these new internationalizing trends, the consequence of scientific invention and technological innovation, to which the nation-state itself is having to adjust. To maintain itself as a primary object of its citizens' loyalty, the government of a modern nation must give them the feeling that it has a "say" on their behalf in decisions that affect their destiny. And if these destiny decisions—the ones that make the difference between ignorance and education, inequality and equality, poverty and prosperity, war and peace—are increasingly taken in and enforced by international organizations, every "national" government will be spending more and more of its time and money trying to qualify as an influential participant in the politics of those organizations.

It is clear enough that even the most influential nation-state can exercise its national influence most effectively from inside—not from outside—international organizations.

What is not clear is how, and how soon, and to what degree, the practical needs for international organization will lead the nations away from overfascination with their conflicts and toward a new preoccupation with their expanding areas of common interest. The degree of world order and international progress which we shall know between now and the end of this century will depend heavily upon the answer to that question. When it comes to the forecasting of weather, the progress is already swift; when it comes to the forestalling of war, the evidence is less persuasive.

As things stand now, the world is fragmented into scores of mostly small and mostly weak nation-states, each trying to pursue its own national interests as it sees them—these plus a handful of "major powers." As things stand now, only these last could qualify as truly influential participants in the international organizations; for to so qualify, a participant must be *big enough* and *rich enough* to contribute significant resources, *willing enough* to see its destiny entangled with that of other peoples, and *skillful enough* to practice effectively, on behalf of its constituents, the new politics of international organization.

Of the world's existing nation-states, only one already comes even close to meeting all these rigorous tests of relevance. The United States of America is big enough and rich enough to bring its resources to bear anywhere in the world —alone or in cooperation with others; most Americans are willing to assume that our destiny is necessarily linked with that of other continents and other peoples; as a consequence, Americans are already major contributors to, and among the most skillful leaders in, half a hundred international organizations. The efforts of other nations, and troupes of nations, to participate with the United States in the making of destiny decisions will be the story of international relations during the rest of this century.

Of the world's other sovereignties, only two are certainly big enough to qualify under present circumstances. Communist China may make up in size and potential what it still lacks in gross national product, but its leaders are still so parochial in their outlook and so clumsy in their international operations that mainland China does not yet meet the other two tests of effectiveness in world politics. The Soviet Union is surely big enough, by any measure, and its leaders certainly see their destiny in international terms; but despite the alleged internationalism of Marxist theory, in practice the Soviet leaders yield to none in their addiction to nationalist dogma and their devotion to "sovereignty"—and so they are, by and large, ineffectual in the politics of international organizations. The Soviets still think that if a nation is big enough and strong enough, it can go its own way. On the basis of their own postwar experience, Americans are justified in coming to the opposite conclusion: the bigger you are, the more you are drawn into everybody else's affairs.

A few other countries might be considered as coming close to qualifying as direct participants in destiny decisions in a world lineup in which the average size of nations is small —and getting still smaller. The United Kingdom has the will and the skill but no longer the economic power required for global influence; Japan and Germany are still inhibited by their history and the lingering resentments of their neighbors from translating growing power into growing international participation. France, which is positioned by its history to lead, is constrained by the notion that the destiny of each nation can be reserved for decision by its leaders without advance international engagements. India and Brazil have the potential but not yet the internal cohesion to wield more than a regional influence.

Beyond these nation-states and a very few others, a hundred nations or more are too wanting in the ingredients of national influence to enable their peoples to feel their governments make a crucial difference in decisions about peace and prosperity. A good many of the smaller states in every continent—from Scandinavia and the Low Countries around to Thailand, the Philippines, Australia, and New Zealand— certainly try to make up in international outlook and hearty participation what they lack in economic size and military power. Insofar as the votes in UN assemblies are crucial to their destiny, the Africans as a group are vigorous participators. And if effective participation in destiny decisions were measured by the noise-level of verbal contributions to international discourse, then a good many nonaligned leaders would certainly qualify. But real decisions are still likely to be made by contributors, not by observers, however vocal.

IV

A key problem for most of the world's peoples, therefore, is how to organize to operate effectively within big organizations, in which the destiny decisions are made: that is, how to make sure they are effectively consulted on nuclear affairs, on arms control, on trade and monetary policies, on the more equitable distribution of the world's resources, on the politics of weather control, on the benefits accruing from atomic energy and space exploration, on arrangements for peacekeeping and peacemaking, and on the growing volume of international rules that guide the penetration of outsiders into matters that used to be regarded as "national" preserves, such as economic growth, social development, and the protection of the inalienable rights of man. The first need of the smaller nations is to be taken seriously on big questions.

In the decades ahead, two trends will operate to modify the present gross disparities between national power and national influence of the great and the small nation-states.

One is that the "major powers" will discover that their own national interests converge more and more with the national interests of others on the great issues and great tasks of our times—that national interests can be pursued most effectively through international organizations, and national purposes can be pursued most effectively through international cooperation. Learning that, they may even come to appreciate more the values that nations and peoples without "power" can contribute to the world's well-being, and to be more grateful for the pluralism of human society and culture. They will see, too, what Americans are beginning, perforce, to understand: that if one or more of the great powers gains too much influence by the contribution of too

great a proportion of the resources of the international community—even in the form of development aid—the basis
for cooperation is eroded and the character of international
organization is blurred.

So the great powers, in their own interests, will increasingly have to identify those interests with the interests of
others and seek to draw them into more robust forms of
partnership.

The other trend that will tend to narrow the "influence
gap" in the international community is that the smaller, and
particularly the smallest, nation-states will somehow have to
combine into larger units with firmer voices. In the foreseeable future we may still see existing nation-states split into
ministates by the divisive passions of tribalism. But the net
trend will be the other way—for such reasons as resources
development, industrialization and trade, and also—perhaps
even more so—to add to their "influence" in the world community.

This is why the trend toward regional unity, already much
in evidence, will certainly continue strong. In the three
decades I am presuming to call the foreseeable future,
Western Europe will probably be forced, by its own urge, to
participate in wider matters of vital interest to Western
Europeans, to continue the amalgamating trend that already
finds expression in advanced forms of economic cooperation
and a common market, and to widen the constituency to
include the British and Scandinavians to the north and west,
and perhaps other peoples to the south and east. (Because
participation in wider world decisions requires a certain degree of likemindedness, there is a necessary limit to
"Europe's" eastern expansion without profound political
change.)

Economics is also the first-stage booster for Latin American unity. But in welding the Latin Americans together, the
major influence is likely to be the political need to deal on

a more nearly equal basis with the North Americans. In Africa and the splintered Arab world, some sense of racial likeness may speed the development of two or three sub-continental units; even today, the fragmented sovereignties of Africa are internationally effective on economic develop-ment, trade policy, and security matters only when they suc-ceed in acting together. In Asia and the Pacific, the regional cooperation is likely to be slow in developing, but India and Japan are two cores of potential strength, and the truculence of the Chinese Communists is already hastening the trend toward regionalism.

During this "foreseeable" period, then, the nation-state will not be withering away. But two other things will be happen-ing. First, small nations, by combining into larger ones, will be redefining what it has to mean to be a nation-state in the third third of the twentieth century. And second, the smaller number of larger "nations" will be internationalizing a growing proportion of all the decisions they make, includ-ing nearly all the really important ones.

V

What issues will predominate in the new politics? Judging by the considerable experience of twenty postwar years, the nation-states or nation-groups will argue and negotiate, agree and disagree, about issues of *function* and of *control*.

As the technological imperative brings more and more subjects into "international relations," the ever widening definition of what is appropriate for international agencies to do will create a great deal of trouble. Most national govern-ments today would resist my conclusion, earlier in this article, that there is anything inherently international about the pro-tection of citizens from aggression by their own government or racial group. But setting standards for other people's be-havior in matters of human rights is an international prospect of growing urgency, and what starts as an effort to influence other people's behavior is more than likely to end by agreement to standards that constrain one's own behavior as well.

Nobody can predict how controversial any particular extension of jurisdiction will be in each of the fifty-three organizations we already belong to, or in the many more that presumably will be established in the remaining years of this century. What does seem to be predictable is that the area of international jurisdiction will grow at something like the speed of scientific and technological change—because the one is a function of the other.

What limits the rate at which public tasks and public policy issues are internationalized? Essentially the "governor" on international systems seems to be the enormous difficulty of deciding who should decide to govern them.

It is these "constitutional issues" that produce the great debates and defections that characterize the life of any lively international organization. The recurring issue over the use of the Security Council veto has regularly enlivened the proceedings of the UN. In recent years the classic battle over the power of the General Assembly to assess its members for peacekeeping operations moved to the UN's center stage; but the issue was the same: could a major power be forced by the votes of other nations to approve a UN operation it regards as contrary to its own interests—or to do itself something it decides it does not want to do?

In the North Atlantic Treaty Organization, still by a wide margin the world's largest peacekeeping force, the recent defection of France from NATO's integrated military organization was touched off by a similar fear that France might be made to do something it might not want to do. There is less automaticity in NATO's response to aggression than is generally believed: each member still has to make its own decision precisely what to do in any given emergency. But peacetime cooperation in establishing an integrated command does create a strong presumption that the allies will act and react together if attacked; it was from this presumption that the French government withdrew in 1966.

The control of international military forces creates hard enough political dilemmas. But some of the civil forms of internationalism are going to present even more excruciating choices between the nostalgia for unfettered independence and the need for international executive operations that impinge deeply on the vital interests of nation-states.

It is easy enough to agree that radio frequencies should be allocated by an international authority—otherwise the confusion on the air waves would be intolerable for all. But when men of one nationality have it in their power to change the weather that controls other men's agriculture and air defense, it will be far more difficult to decide who should decide what. And in the tortured field of disarmament, the end question is: Who keeps peace in a disarmed world? What kind of executive—with what punitive powers—under what form of legislative control—should have the power to bring major nation-states to heel?

As a final example, the poor nations seek a constantly widening international control over the transfer of resources from the rich nations. Taken together, the international funds and banks are now the world's biggest aid program. As they grow, the concerted effort by the net recipients of benefits to dominate the system will create a widening constitutional crisis with the net contributors. The international executives will have to be far-sighted enough to serve as the "liberal center," preventing either recipients or contributors from "winning" the battle for control.

By and large, two ways of making collective decisions have been worked out by mankind to make cooperation possible where no person or group can be trusted to make the ultimate decision. One is the UN way—to count national noses, sometimes weighing the count because the noses are of varying shapes and sizes. Large countries often get permanent seats, or special voting rights, on governing bodies —precisely to prevent the sovereign equality of nations from producing actions that are ridiculously out of touch with the realities of power. (Where the "action" is merely an expression of opinion, as often in the UN General Assembly, the big nations have learned to swallow and smile when they do not agree.)

The other method is that of consensus, as practiced for example in NATO. The North Atlantic Council never votes. If everybody agrees, the Council acts; if everybody does not agree, the Council often creates some formula whereby those who want to act can act together without unanimous consent. Thus when France withdrew her military cooperation but stayed in the Alliance (and thus in the fifteen-nation North Atlantic Council) the other members set up a fourteen-nation council called the Defense Planning Committee to make all decisions affecting the integrated defense of the NATO area and went right ahead with plans to modernize NATO strategy.

Neither the UN nor the NATO solution to the dilemmas of international governance is "best," and there are dozens of conceivable variants of each. The new politics will have to produce tailor-made solutions to each puzzle as it appears. If more and more international decisions are a technological "must," the ingenuity of man is equal to the task of contriving decision-making systems that most people think are fair, most of the time.

5

URBAN PROBLEMS AND GROUP RELATIONS

ROBERT C. WEAVER

Secretary of Housing and Urban Development

U RBAN GROWTH is an inevitable consequence of contemporary population growth. Men have nearly always lived in communities but never before to the extent that they do now, and by all accounts and projections the pace of urban growth will accelerate and continue to set precedents as far in the future as men can see.

The accelerating pace of urbanization since the beginning of this century is unmistakable, and it is a worldwide phenomenon. In these years, the world's population has grown 50 percent, its urban population has grown 240 percent, its largest cities 260 percent.[1] There is nothing to indicate that the pace will not continue. In the United States, the population, presently nearing 200 million, is projected to reach 400 million in half a century, with 320 million of our people living in urban communities.

The future of man is therefore largely an urban future. There is little reason to question the quantity of urbanizing that will take place. There is every reason to be concerned over whether men can gain the knowledge and the skills

[1] The White House Conference on International Cooperation, Report of the Committee on Urban Development, Nov. 28–Dec. 1, 1965, Exhibit II.

[85]

to shape events in such a way as to preserve and enhance the quality of urban living.

Typically today in urban problems, as in many problems, there is a widespread yearning for some single or simple solution, no matter how complex or diverse the elements may be. No matter how stubbornly intertwined the forces may be, the search goes on, by some at least, for the single strand that would, when given the proper pull, unravel even a seamless web.

But among thoughtful observers, the urban condition is increasingly recognized for its multiplicity of problems. They are the problems of people and their needs for satisfaction in shelter, employment, education, health, transportation, entertainment, culture, and many other factors. Their very delineation is a step toward a strategy of solutions. It is a step toward gaining an understanding that while each is a field for specialization in itself, the interrelationship of all is still another field worthy of specialization.

To view them as an interrelated whole, nevertheless, presupposes an understanding of each, the complexities, subtleties, paradoxes—and the heritages containing both good and ill. Among the ills, poverty and racial discrimination are but two factors in the cantankerous and individualistic histories of urban communities, but they are so important among all aspects that they are sometimes confused with the whole of urban problems.

There are, of course, other problems in the urban environment of the United States than the problems of the nonwhite in the city. There are problems of governmental organization, adequate provision of community facilities, bringing open space and beauty to the city, training professional and technical personnel, and a great many others.[2] It is well to keep in mind that even where poverty can be eliminated and

---

[2] For a fuller discussion see "Cities in Crisis," by the author, in *The Troubled Environment*, a symposium sponsored in 1965 by Urban America, Inc.

where racial discrimination can be overcome, serious urban problems remain.

It is also true, however, that the elimination of poverty and the overcoming of racial barriers will involve nearly every aspect of the urban condition. It will require an understanding of their interrelated characters. Their solutions would be perhaps the most important actions that could be taken to preserve and restore the human values of urban settings and to create healthy and thriving communities.

The future of the city is inextricably related to the future of the urban poor. At this moment in time, the single most striking fact about the American city is that its fate is indivisible from the fate of the American Negro. The ultimate test of the American city is whether it can achieve a balanced growth that provides full and equal opportunity and participation for the Negroes. They are the most sizable minority grouping that does not share freely in American social and economic life. But this condition applies in commensurate degree as well to such smaller minority groups as the Mexicans, Puerto Ricans, Indians, and migrant laborers.

It should be made clear that a reference to the city in this context means not only the central or inner city but the suburbs, the metropolitan regions surrounding cities, and the urbanizing fringe areas beyond. There are no solutions for any of them that do not affect the others and do not depend on the others.

Parenthetically it might be said that the ecology of urban regions, that is, the interrelated character of the central city, metropolitan region, and the newly urbanizing areas, is not well understood and that it represents one of many subjects among urban problems where knowledge is still as yet at a frontier.

II

Many efforts are under way to extend and broaden knowledge in urban affairs, particularly in the area of group relations in urban settings. These are attempts to penetrate the surfaces, and they often pose challenges to conventional wisdom. An example is a recent attempt to learn more about the actual conditions of the people who are being supported, in part at least, by welfare programs assisted by the federal government. There are, this study showed, some 7.3 million Americans now on federally assisted welfare rolls. On the basis of traditional thinking, it would have been a typical guess that some number of millions of these persons could be made employable and self-sufficient by a suitable combination of job training and education programs.

What the study actually revealed, however, is that only 50,000 males were capable of benefiting from such programs. Of the others, 2.1 million, mostly women, are more than sixty-five years old; 700,000 are blind or otherwise severely handicapped; 3.5 million are children whose parents cannot support them; the remaining 1 million are the parents of these children, including 9,000,000 mothers and 150,000 are fathers, and two-thirds of the latter are also incapacitated in one way or another.[3]

It is significant that we are only now beginning to get the kind of knowledge revealed by this preliminary study. But the important point to be made here is that this knowledge raises new questions about how the traditional thinking on making the poor self-sufficient needs to be reevaluated in terms of actual conditions revealed by new knowledge.

Similarly, it raises questions about how to motivate the people who live in slums and racial ghettos, wherever they are in the world, who feel lost and alienated from the rest of society but who are capable of full participation in the larger environment. Clearly, exhortation alone would not be effective. Certainly, the approach must be one that involves these

[3] Reported by Joseph A. Califano, Jr., special assistant to President Johnson, address to Washington chapter, Sigma Delta Chi, Apr. 19, 1967, unpublished text, p. 6.

people in a meaningful participation. This is not done simply, and it will require modification of attitudes, values, and behavior, as well as perfection of techniques in communication.

Much has been written about the subculture of the slums and racial ghettos. My own contribution began twenty years ago with the first comprehensive analysis of racial residential segregation.[4] The reformulation of the problems twenty years later does not involve any basic reversal of philosophy or any retreat from the goals expressed. It does of course involve changes in strategy, tactics, and priorities resulting not only from the dramatic events of these years in the pursuit of civil rights but also from new knowledge that has been attained by a variety of research.

Still, there is a widespread tendency to look upon the residents of a ghetto as a homogeneous group though the civil rights movement and the social sciences have clearly demonstrated the fallacy of that simplistic view. The ghetto has many elements among its residents. They range in values from what might be called the "respectable poor" who are often vehemently middle class in their values to another extreme element that repudiates middle-class concepts and middle-class behavior. And there are many variations between.

We do know that there is a subculture in the ghetto and that its values are significantly different from the dominant ones. We shall have to take this into account, examining the nature, incidence, and peculiarities of the subculture, and the various shades of difference in values and behavior patterns.

It is clear then, in my view, that here are two areas where further knowledge is vital: the characteristics of the urban poor, their physical, mental, and social capacities for full participation in society; and their attitudes, values, and

[4] Robert C. Weaver, *The Negro Ghetto* (New York: Harcourt, Brace & Co., 1948). Reissued in 1967 by Russell & Russell.

behavior patterns toward the whole of society. Without attempting to assert that these exhaust the list, I will move on in this selective discussion to observe that personal traits must be viewed in relation to the movements of people and their mobility.

III

There has been particular concern in the United States for some years now that the population of core areas of many cities has been declining while the immediate suburban populations are rising rapidly. Increasingly also the poor and disadvantaged are becoming concentrated in central cities, while the suburbs are inhabited almost exclusively by the middle class.

In a nation in which the general level of affluence is unprecedentedly high, enclaves of poverty in the cores of cities are increasingly visible to all but especially to their virtual prisoners, to whom they are intolerable and a source of tension and explosion.

There is, in one sense, contained within the United States an underdeveloped nation consisting of thirty million poor persons, about a third of them nonwhites. Among the poor, a principal and significant difference between whites and nonwhites, for this discussion, is that the nonwhites are relegated to a segment of the housing market. There can be no true equality of opportunity so long as that condition remains.

The limited choice of housing shapes a number of problems. It artificially inflates the cost of shelter in the slums. It mandates *de facto* segregation of public schools. It limits job opportunities. It erects the barriers within which a subculture of tension festers.

The desire to equalize opportunity and to foster residential integration does not require, however, that these areas of nonwhite concentration be abandoned, nor does it require that those who elect to live in them be denied the opportunity to do so. We cannot espouse freedom of choice and simultaneously deny it to any group. There are, in many cities, large ethnic neighborhoods that are maintained on a wholly voluntary basis.

What is required is the eradication of artificial barriers to free movement in the housing market, and concurrently, the upgrading of life in the neighborhoods that have been so long neglected. As a consequence of action in both directions, not only will nonwhites have greater residential mobility but they will also enjoy improved capabilities and status wherever they reside.

Laws alone, however effectively enforced, will not bring this about any more than wishing for it, however piously, will make a change. To change racial residential patterns will require motivation and action across a broad range of fronts, and I believe the decisive factor will be economic mobility. The effort to press for a public policy of free and open occupancy must be joined by a variety of efforts to expand nonwhite participation in all other phases of American life but particularly in jobs and education as well as political action.

Improvement of the conditions in the slums and freedom of movement out of them are not inconsistent. They are mutually supporting. The ghettos cannot be made livable and attractive unless there is an appreciable increase in mobility for nonwhites. The sheer pressure of numbers from population growth will eventually damn the ghettos, and further in-migration confounds the situation.

Economic pressures equal the physical pressures. There will never be enough, or sufficient diversity, of jobs in the ghetto to meet the requirements of its residents. The majority of nonwhites now employed find jobs outside their areas of residence. It is well documented that the incidence of unemployment among Negroes is far higher than among whites. And the unfortunate truth is that segregated schools perpetuate color distinctions no less than they respond to them. The traditional function of the public school to enhance mobility has broken down in the slums.

Programs for job training, job availability, improved education, and all types of human rehabilitation will be involved over the long range. A short-term solution can be employment and apprenticeship programs in the physical rehabilitation of the ghetto itself. However, a time will come when a great majority of those engaged in rehabilitating the ghetto will have to find other work. It is important to recognize the temporary nature of ghetto employment and the corresponding necessity to expand job opportunities.

On-the-job training programs are vitally important, but they are presently few in number inside the ghettos. Much of this type of work is not only outside the ghetto but outside the central city, and often it is not accessible by public transportation. If there are to be—as there must be—greater employment opportunities for nonwhites, they must have access to housing beyond the central cities, too. Job mobility requires residential mobility as well.

IV

The ultimate goals for urban areas are easily stated in broad terms: equal opportunity and maximum freedom of choice; the highest possible standard of living; the most attractive and economically viable environments; reduction of substandard housing, crime, delinquency, and human want; assurance of human dignity and a high sense of personal worth; reestablishment of free public education as an effective instrument for economic and social mobility as well as psychological health.

Ghetto patterns are sooner or later inconsistent with most of these goals. They complicate the achievement of all of them. Yet it is crucial not to confuse ultimate goals with intermediate steps. There are those who hypothesize that nothing can be done to move toward the goals until the ghetto patterns are eradicated. This is unrealistic, and for the simple reason that there is literally nowhere else for the ghetto residents to go while the eradication takes place.

There are others—the Black Nationalists—who consciously or unconsciously believe that enforced segregation and submerged status cannot be changed, and they retreat to an untenable position that a closed, self-sufficient black society can be maintained. Finally, there are those who assert that any attempt to improve the ghetto merely perpetuates it, and they therefore oppose any such efforts. They, too, are unrealistic. Few of them have felt the pulse of immediacy that haunts most disadvantaged nonwhites, whose concern is for a decent home, a good school, better municipal services, a more attractive environment, assistance in getting a good job, and effective aid in social problems.

Between now and the time that they have free access to housing throughout the urban complex, the mass of nonwhites want action. Without being economists, they know that there is little low-income housing in suburbia. They realize that access to hotels, theaters, restaurants, and the like is a meaningless right so long as they have insufficient money for admission. Many are not sure that their children are best served by being bused to schools in hostile neighborhoods. And many of them appreciate that their ghetto areas are often so well situated near the center of cities that they now inhabit potentially valuable urban real estate.

To say to them that nothing substantial can or should be done in the ghetto, or to insist that no low-income housing should be built or rehabilitated where they live, is to articulate a position they will not accept. They are committed to doing something about the ghetto. They resent the limitations now imposed. They want equal opportunity. But they won't wait for housing integration—which means little in the present housing market because of their incomes—before changes are made.[5]

There are substantial efforts underway, or being planned, to move beyond long-continuing efforts to improve cities by public housing and urban renewal—to move to a posture of preserving and improving entire neighborhoods that have been neglected. These efforts involve governments at all levels, private industry, universities, and a variety of non-profit interests. These efforts extend both to physical facilities and to human welfare.

One of the newest prospects for augmenting the supply of low- and moderate-income housing in suburbia is the development of entirely new communities planned from the beginning to embrace housing for many income levels. This presupposes strong public policy and participation, for otherwise, new communities will generally cater to higher-income families.

The new communities, however, can be effective instruments for racial integration. They are much like the concepts of educational parks for central cities, these parks being planned from the beginning to be large enough to draw students from so much of the community that they will inevitably be integrated. Until recently, the articulation of such a possibility was tantamount to destroying public support for it. Today, however, both of these concepts are freely and widely discussed. In the concept of new communities, it is possible to require a multi-income and a multi-ethnic participation as a condition for federal involvement.

V

There is no paucity of prophets of doom on the urban scene. But this is not new. Cities have been abused and

---

[5] For a discussion of this problem in greater depth, see the author's *Dilemmas of Urban America* (Cambridge, Mass.: Harvard University Press, 1966), Chap. 4.

relegated to destruction by myopic foreseers since their beginnings. In this nation there are those who hanker for a rural past and still equate urbanity with evil. There are others who observe urban deficiencies and cannot see any other solution than abandonment. All of the naysayers ignore the investment of the city, its markets, its diversity of services, and its unique capacity, as August Heckscher has put it, to be "the home of the arts" as well as "a work of art itself."[6]

American cities have a particular tradition. It was to our cities that waves of immigrants moved, and it was largely in them that the acculturation of newcomers occurred. In the process, these new Americans were prepared to enter the full potential of American society. Thus, the city has been, in this and every nation, as Charles Abrams phrased it, the "concourse of the various—in faces, in trade, in the exchange of thought, and in the potentials for leadership."[7]

Cities are the creation of man, and since most of their problems are man-made, man also has the capacity to deal with them. Three basic ingredients will be required—additional resources, additional knowledge, and additional trained personnel.

What the total cost will be cannot be determined now. It will vary in response to our successes in developing technology, modifying institutions to permit application of new approaches, increasing and redistributing incomes, learning how to deal effectively with social and human problems, and improving the quality of administration.

Research and development still have not produced a basic foundation in urban knowledge or a systematic inquiry into new techniques, materials, and methods in home building or urban transit systems or other community facilities. It is my hope that a major research program will be funded by our

[6] August Heckscher, "A New Universe of Creativity," *The General Electric Forum*, Jan.–Mar., 1967, pp. 7–8.
[7] Charles Abrams, "Downtown Decay and Revival," *Journal of the American Institute of Planners*, Feb., 1961, p. 9.

national government in these areas. At the same time, American manufacturing firms generally have far surpassed the home-building industry in research.[8] If the building industry followed the general pattern, it would devote 2 percent of receipts to this endeavor, and if it did, this would mean $300 million by 1975—far beyond the present level of effort.

The third basic need—for trained people—is a fairly universal deficiency, involving a lack of generalists as well as specialists and including operating personnel at all levels, within government and outside it. Today it is difficult to recruit the talent required to administer existing programs at their relatively low level of funding. It is inconceivable that we could successfully operate an effort of much greater magnitude without a much larger component of administrators, research workers, operators, and consultants.

The American city today is both witness and participant as massive social and economic changes cause a drastic alteration of our society. But, as noted in the beginning, the process of urbanization is worldwide. No two cities anywhere are identical, but all have their individual components of economic, political, and social problems. The tensions between economic classes are universal, and those tensions are becoming increasingly urban tensions.

This nation attempts to meet its troubles through the joint efforts of private enterprise and government. This is neither the easiest nor the most direct approach. But it does contain the potential for ultimate efficacy and maximum freedom. In the end, this approach, with all its detours, will have been worthwhile only if the freedoms become available to the least advantaged as well as all others.

---

[8] Leonard A. Lecht, *Goals, Priorities, and Dollars* (New York: The Free Press, 1966), p. 202.

6

ART FOR A CHANGING SCALE

GYORGY KEPES

School of Architecture and Planning
Massachusetts Institute of Technology

T HE NINETEENTH CENTURY came to its end in an explosion of human knowledge and human energies overwhelming in its consequences. A new world rapidly took shape as the physical environment became transformed. Agriculture and industry underwent enormous expansion. World population multiplied. Cities became giant spreading tangles of soaring buildings, roaring traffic, and bustling humanity. Space shrunk as the upper air became a realm of superfast transport. Time grew enormously as the origins of the universe were put further, further, and further back, and measured intervals of time became fantastically minute slices. Rapid advances took place in every field of technology. Social relations were disrupted by a cycle of wars and revolutions. The unprecedented scale and speed of the new events were major factors in the inevitable disorientation as people endeavored to face and solve their problems.

Thus the advent of the twentieth century did not resolve the conflicts of the nineteenth century; it exacerbated them. Our century still faces the same problems that early industrialization left in its wake, and on a tremendously exploded scale. Slums and machine-regimented human work are ruthlessly invading the most distant corners of the globe. Industrialization, urbanization, mechanization, westernization, and mass production have reached into India, China, Africa, and the South Seas. As in the past, the process of alleviating material misery generates toxic by-products, and the degree to which the harmful by-products, can be avoided or neutralized depends upon the quality of our life. We cannot, like Ivan Karamazov, return our entrance ticket to life because it was bought by the suffering of the innocent. We have to accept twentieth-century conditions, but we also have to learn how to make optimal use of them. The intensity of life, the splendor of solidarity, the faith and wisdom of age-old customs, the pride in making things expressed in folk art, folk songs, the dignity of a fully lived life, all are clearly endangered by the invasion of our half-understood, potent technical tools. Can we translate these qualities of the smaller-scale life to the new amplified scale? No doubt each scale has its own structural solution, its own pattern of values. To retain the values of the past without recognizing the structure of the present is to undertake sentimental adventures that will surely falter. The poetry of our new scale, the faith, the order, the pride and splendor of today, come only from a full grasp of what makes our age.

Whatever the magnitude and complexity of the world, the artistic imagination still feeds back information to the central scale of human values. The individual is still dependent on the work of his hands for biological and psychic health. It is still through those hands that he is materially involved in his world. The nineteenth century increasingly emphasized work as a justification of existence, an inner guide and compass, the raw material of social progress. Leading nineteenth-century scientists and social thinkers recognized the propelling force of work in the evolutionary process, both biological and social, and based their essential argument about society on the premise of a conflict in the distribution of the values produced by labor. As early as 1831 Carlyle was able to recognize the constructive aspects of the industrial world and accept productivity as the key to existing and forthcoming values:

> Hast thou heard, with sound ears, the awakening of a Manchester, on Monday morning, at half-past five by the clock; the rushing off of its thousand mills, like the boom of an Atlantic tide, ten thousand spools and spindles all set humming there—it is perhaps, if thou knew it well, sublime as a Niagara, or more so. Cotton-spinning is the clothing of the naked in its result; the triumph of man over matter in its means. Soot and despair are not the essence of it: they are divisible from it.

As the division of labor grew, the greater grew the cleavage between work as a creative process and as drudgery that corrodes man's confidence in his role in life. When the individual was no longer able to participate in all the steps of the metamorphosis of raw material into created object, work lost meaning, honesty, and basic significance. Blake, Ruskin, Morris, Tolstoy, and Rodin were only a few among the passionate voices that rose against distortion of human work. As Ruskin hoped:

> It would be a part of my scheme of physical education if every youth in the state, from the king's son downwards, should learn to do something finally and thoroughly with the hand, so as to let him know what touch meant; and what stout craftsmanship meant.

William Morris commented:

> There is no square mile of the earth's surface that is not beautiful in its own way if we men will only abstain from willfully destroying that beauty; and it is this reasonable share in the beauty of the earth that I claim is the right of every man who will earn it by due labor.

In the ever growing complexity of the industrial world, the attenuation of the creative aspect of human work has increasingly taken away basic nourishment. The farther away we get from a fully lived, productive life, the higher rises the heap of roadblocks to health and true self-realization. In the nineteenth century most of the courageous spokesmen against these ills were Utopians—unrealistic and sentimental in the ways they suggested for reducing inner tensions. Like the aging Tolstoy, they were willing to sacrifice the technological base of the modern world for a sentimentalized primitive life as direct and simple as the Sermon on the Mount. But no matter whether they sought redemption or social therapy, they understood that it is humanity's birthright to work. The birthright of labor, as Morris put it, is the joy of labor.

Domestication of the most obvious dynamics of the twentieth-century world had its earliest and strongest hold in Italy. Lagging behind industrially, the restless young Italians glorified the dynamic new wonders, which were, for them, a dream. Their glimpses of the new technical life were tempting; and, in addition, history made advanced techniques supremely welcome to life-hungry Italian intellectuals. Italy was the country of museums, the guardian of past richness, richness with no immediate relevance for the twentieth-century man seeking his own identity. One can hardly imagine a more acute contrast than a racing car tearing through the narrow, beautiful streets of medieval Siena. Electricity, the airplane, the motor car, and the many other emblems of twentieth-century technical power hardly seem comfortable alongside the memories of the more climactic richness of past artistic efforts.

To the generation of Italians at the beginning of the twentieth century, it seemed that the two worlds could not coexist and that to live and to live up to the twentieth-century potentials it was necessary to blast away all the inhibiting memories of the past. "Let's kill the moonlight," declared one of the futurist manifestos. The violence, vitality, and brutality of the technical tools and the beast in man became the new ideals. Painters and sculptors hero-worshiped speed and motion. They dreamed of a complete rebirth, a new strength, completely divorced from the past. Boccioni, a gifted and sincere artist, commented in one of his letters, "Our primitivism should have nothing in common with that of antiquity. Our primitivism is the extreme climax of complexity, whereas the primitivism of antiquity is the bubbling of simplicity."[1]

The artist-poets felt that their task was to find ways in which to structure a new scale of the world. Boccioni's "climax of complexity" expressed the new scale and the concomitant task of bringing the new wealth and dynamics into meaningful order. The old walls, the old spaces, the old motives and reminiscences of antiquity seemed only handicaps. Again, to quote Boccioni, "I have tried for a great synthesis of labor, light and movement."[2]

The nineteenth-century dreams of Turner and Constable to return light and movement to the dark, smoke-ridden industrial towns, and William Morris' dream of restoring human dignity to human labor were reformulated in twentieth-century terms. In certain ways these were reduced to mere acrobatics of the explosive spirit of ennui. The nineteenth-century dreams of light, color, motion, and work had an ethical overtone, an ideal behind it. The futurist hero worship of dynamics was basically a technical enterprise to record and absorb the new perceptual task of the twentieth-century industrial world but without any clear inner compass of what to do with it or how to use it. Though their limitations and the inherent traps in the material with which they

1 Letter to Vicco Baier, 1913.
2 Letter to the director of the Galeria d'Arte Moderna, Venice.

worked led some of them to the Fascist worship of power, still their work prepared a climate of awareness. They pioneered in a new visual language that could express the intensity of experience of the dynamic new technical world. The road from the first motor car to the first visual turmoil in the cities, to airplanes and present supersonic flight, has been uninterrupted.

The Italian futurists were not alone in responding to the technical world. Observing eyes in France and Russia also read the promise of the new visual environment. Each country and cultural background brought forth its own interpretation and emphasis.

In France, under the influence of the Italians, Guillaume Apollinaire, the poet, led an aggressive attack on the past, beginning with the inherited structure of language. Like the Italian Marinetti, he wished to destroy syntax, get rid of adjectives and punctuation, leaving only the most elementary patterning of sound and words. The two men held the belief that the new quality of intensity of their age could not be presented with the outdated tools of language, and therefore an essential first step was to chop away all unnecessary historical barnacles.

The Russian futurists, including Mayakovsky and his friends, started with the same wild destructive spirit. They, too, rejected all memories of the past and acted on the words of their manifesto that "the Academy and Pushkin are more unintelligible than hieroglyphs." But quite soon their personal intensity and the background of a fermenting social world gave them a purposeful direction. Mayakovsky aimed also at a new simplicity and at strength, but in his confidence and exuberance he wished to shift the focus from the machine to man. His dynamics had, as a goal, to spur mankind to a fast conquest of physical power geared to human needs. Man, nature, and technical power were to be brought together in a broadening scale that would enrich human life.

The sunbeams we shall tie
In radiant brooms, and sweep
Clouds from the sky
With electricity.
We shall make honey-sweet the rivers of the worlds.
The streets of earth we'll pave with radiant stars.[3]

The creative energies of liberated man would open up a new scale of life in which friendship with nature would be deepened.

The romantic dreams of Shelley, the all-embracing luminous space of Turner, had echoes as short-lived as the original dreams themselves. The expression of life exalted aggressive movement, noise, and speed; as Marinetti put it, "The racing space, the acrobat somersault, the slap in the face and the blow of the fist . . . war, the bloody and necessary test of the people's force." The new challenge of a bigger, faster, and potentially richer world found its caricature in the cult of crude sensation, in a bombastic journalistic hero worship of twentieth-century dynamic hardware—the car, the machine gun, the airplane.

The challenge of the new cannot be met by merely giving in to what is new, by a sheer mirroring of novel kinetic excitement. Without a sense of the deepest roots and a total, broad awareness, the menacing power of the man-created world is treated with the same respect that a child gives to a firecracker or roller-coaster ride. To face the new scale there must be an acceptance of both the old and new, the immediate and the distant, the inner and outer world, and an awareness of their interconnections.

A simultaneous awareness of dimensions on a multiple scale is essential if the moment of today and the projected

[3] Vladimir Mayakovsky, *Mystery-Bouffe*, trans. by George Rapall Noyes and Alexander Kaun, in *Masterpieces of the Russian Drama*, ed. George Rapall Noyes (New York: Dover Publications, 1961), II, 879. Reprinted through permission of the publisher.

purpose of tomorrow are to coexist. Saint-Exupéry, a sensitive observer of the challenge of our broadening vistas commented, "If the traveler, climbing a mountain toward a star, becomes too absorbed in the problem of climbing, he may forget which star is guiding him. If he moves only for the sake of movement he will reach no destination." Our age is characterized by the disjunction in our awareness of the immediate and the subsequent. We seem moved by a tremendous kinetic inertia that pushes us ahead without forethought of where we are going or willingness to check our directions. We have inherited concepts of order belonging to a smaller scale of existence; these are becoming increasingly useless in the explosive new scale of events. We have been accustomed to making ordered relationships by mapping objects and even individuals in their positions relative to one another. Now we are forced to recognize that objects do not have final, unchangeable positions, that human relationships are among the things in the man-created environment that have direction and velocity. The world is energies in interaction. We have to recognize that a description of position tells only half the story. If we see a still photograph of a heavily trafficked street, we find it difficult to tell which cars are in motion and which are standing still. Our information must include velocity as well as position if we are to order the situation. Similarly, in the kinetic situation of today, changing social forces in hitherto neglected areas of the world are posing the demand for an understanding of the dynamic new economic processes. Our understanding can be meaningful only if position, direction, and velocity of the processes are related.

To structure our chaotic environment as well as our knowledge and values, we have to accept the conditions of the new scale and learn to use the tools that have grown from it. Both the world we create inside our heads and the world we create outside our bodies have one basic objective: to preserve the condition of life. We ourselves and our tremendously extended feelers of sensibilities, tools of observation, structures that shelter and give us physical comfort, have, in the final analysis, one objective—to preserve the condition of life in our internal environment, not only in the biological-physiological sense but in the deepest human sense. Our human system, if we may so call it, is a network of interacting variables that has some power of regulating itself in its own experiences. Life and death depend upon our power to regulate the forces that we create.

The artistic sensibility and imaginative act are key factors in regulating the interacting variables of our man-created inner and outer worlds. Artistic sensibility is now seeking new images that will give us our bearings. As the nineteenth-century creative vision projected the images of health and fullness, light, space, and color, and the inner richness of a fully lived life, so twentieth-century artistic sensibility is trying to read the signs between life as it is and life as it could be, and to create vigorous images of order that can domesticate the centrifugal forces of daily life.

The opening of new scientific vistas has widened the physical dimensions of our environment through new forms of transportation and new modes of communication. The implication of these new dynamic dimensions and the potential structure of the new scale of things was the essential theme of the creative imagination. One of the great visionaries of the nineteenth century, Friedrich Nietzsche, put it clearly when he said, "He who one day teacheth men to fly will have shifted all landmarks; to him will all landmarks themselves fly into the air; the earth will he christen anew—as 'the light body.' "[4]

To find one's way in the new dimensions, one has to rename the paths of the universe and set new frames of reference and orientation. The twentieth century brought with it great

[4] *Thus Spake Zarathustra*, Discourse LV, No. 2, in *Complete Works*, Oscar Levy, ed., X (New York: The Macmillan Co., 1911), 235.

promises not only to secure safer conditions for human existence but a greater range for the human spirit through un-
obstructed vistas and new freedom of vision. But the vistas
began to increase faster than vision could encompass them.
It can happen in nature that the woods grow so abundantly
that all sunlight is cut off from the struggling seedling. In
the same way the tremendous growth of knowledge threw a
deepening shadow on many of the early attempts at orientation in this new world.

To use a simple illustration from our daily life, the
increasing number of people whom we meet and with whom
we are acquainted through picture magazines, television,
newsreels, photography, and the new tempo of traveling has
made it increasingly difficult to keep sufficient intimacy in
our contacts to develop true friendships. In fact, in certain
strata of our society, the density and complexity of the daily
routine have made almost a farce of the meaning of friendship. In a similar way, our relation to the environment, to
the city we live in, has become thinner and thinner. So has
the intimate sense of belonging that gave some ages civic
pride in civic achievements.

The many things we know and the many things we know
about suggest a similar situation in knowledge. Our orientation is affected by the tremendous number of possible vistas
that man has opened through conceptual and perceptual tools.
Things hitherto unseen by the unaided eye now offer, through
new instrumentation and such new aids to memory as photo-
graphic emulsion, a vast, complex perspective.

On a more fundamental level we are able to produce and
release energies on a scale that keeps us in fearful suspense.
The tools of preserving life and the tools of destroying life
are terrifying in magnitude. The population expansion, with
all its unresolved future dangers, or "overkill," a term with
devastating implications, implies that there is a power within
human hands that must now be keyed to a meaningful scale

of values. There is no doubt that, given the present pace of inventive power, we have been losing our perspective of knowledge, our bearings, our sense of belonging, our discipline of vision.

From whatever direction we observe the contemporary scene, its most obvious characteristic is incredible acceleration in scale of magnitude, rate of change, and complexity of interrelationships in scientific, technical, and social realms. Just as the political sphere is expanding its areas of interconnection, so every region of the globe is becoming touched by some economic tie from another distant region. This interpenetration of economic spheres is underscored and amplified by vast improvements in techniques of transportation and communication.

The common problem that arises in the attempt to readjust to the increased dimensions is the need to read the characteristics of each level without losing sight of the connecting links among the many levels. To take an everyday example of this problem, we change space context and speed of motion in abrupt, unconnected ways when we move in a big city. To step from an automobile into a subway is to shift not only vistas but dimensions of awareness and scale of orientation. In this and in all similar daily experiences, there is a confusing fabric of response to the surroundings. In an automobile one may sit next to a friend, while at the same time images of the surroundings race past the perceiving eye like a wild motion picture. In the subway one is in close physical proximity to an array of strange faces and unknown lives, all traveling in the same direction but without any obvious visual signals to mark the path. The continual change of scale is further accented by sudden shifts in the spatial setting, from the intimacy of the home to the turmoil of a busy street or the impersonal pattern and segmentation of office space.

These simple, everyday experiences give only a faint hint of the multidimensional kinetics of other scale changes that we hear and read about. The astronaut who sits in a closed space capsule becomes quickly invisible to the naked eye and relies on instrument communication as he races through space. The instruments by which his flight is maintained, guided, and observed are, to a great extent, reduced to a microscale beyond the ability of the unaided eyes to decipher. The span of distances, the velocity of travel, the visible vistas are in a continuous mobile field, shifting from one range to another. These dynamic scale changes could lead to complete disorientation if we did not have tools to master them. And the great significance is that most of the new scientific concepts and technical invention are instruments useful in gauging the new scale of knowledge and existence. It was observed a long time ago that each scale level has its own structure of perception and meaning, but only our century has formulated the knowledge into usable conceptual tools.

Locke, in his *Essay on Human Understanding*, commented that

> . . . were the senses acute enough to discern the minute particles of bodies, and the real constitution on which their sensible qualities depend, I doubt not but they would produce quite different ideas in us . . . and that which is the yellow color of gold, would then disappear and instead of it we could see an admirable texture of parts of a certain size and figure.

We know today that qualities of our sense experience—soft, sweet, sour, bright, or dark—are projections of certain scale events in other scale regions. We have to accept the substances of our environment in their proper scale, meaning that our conceptual grasp of observable events in the physical world has to be recognized as the result of scale orbits of knowledge. "The accuracy of prediction is proportional to the knowledge of the totality in which an event occurs (which surrounds an event)," as Heisenberg, a leading physicist, observed. In fact, as he recognized, it is impossible to make an accurate survey of a particle or set of particles of atomic or subatomic sizes. That is, our tools cannot reach beyond certain minute magnitudes, and this limitation also limits our observation of scale interaction. The "uncertainty principle" of Heisenberg is not just a negative principle; it is also a tool attuned to scale levels. In a burst of events, the first few years of this century formed connecting links between the physical environment on the one hand and different ranges of knowledge and feeling on the other. There were new discoveries relating the unaided senses, new bridges built between hitherto unconnected concepts of the inquiring mind and between the creative imagination and the new tools of machine technology. Cézanne's famous letter to Emil Bernard in 1904 from Aix-en-Provence underlines this development:

> . . . my project of doing Poussin entirely from nature and not constructed piecemeal from notes, drawings and fragments of studies; in short, of painting a living Poussin in the open air, with color and light instead of one of those works imagined in a studio where everything has a brown color of feeble daylight, without reflections from the sky and the sun . . .

Here, Cézanne indicated an essential task of his time: to find continuity with the great intellectual achievements of the past and at the same time to readjust those achievements to direct contact with the present, even in the level of "the little sensations of the eye," tapping rich sources of visual joy and strength. He wished not only to correlate the past and present but to weave the intellect and the senses into a single fabric.

Some of Cézanne's great contemporaries touched upon this same theme of tying together artistic response and a broad intellectual questioning of the world. The potent new tools of industry were first feared and rejected by the intellectual Luddites. Ruskin and Morris more than doubted the possibility of making the machine a successful creative tool and rejected any hopes of domesticating the new beasts. But in 1902 Frank Lloyd Wright, with clear and courageous vision, declared a new union of art and technology in a lecture at Hull House:

> Is it not more likely that the medium of artistic expression itself has changed and broadened until a new definition and a new direction must be given the art activity of the future, and that the machine has finally made for the artist, whether he will own it yet or not, a splendid distinction between the art of old and art to come? A distinction made by the tool which frees human labor, lengthens and broadens the life of the simplest man and thereby the basis of the democracy upon which we insist.
>
> If the art of the Greek, produced at such cost to human life, was so noble and enduring, what limit dare we now imagine to an art based upon an adequate life for the individual?[5]

The hopeful visions of the artist and the architect were able to accept the broadened scene. They were able to connect the past and present order of life, the power of the new technology and creative vision. But they were not alone in their confidence in the new tools of industry. Some of the scientists at the turn of the century were more than ready to expect from the vistas of their own field rich new resources for creative vision.

In 1902, the same year in which Wright wrote "The Art and Craft of the Machine," Michelson, the first American to receive the Nobel prize in physics, accepted the new scientific and technical dimensions of the twentieth century as legitimate tools and goals for artistic image making:

---

[5] "The Art and Craft of the Machine," Frank Lloyd Wright, *Writings and Buildings*, ed. by *Edgar Kaufmann and Ben Raeburn* (New York: Horizon Press, Inc., 1960), pp. 60, 70.

Indeed, so strongly do these color phenomena appeal to me that I venture to predict that in the not very distant future there may be a color art analogous to the art of sound—a *color music*, in which the performer, seated before a literally chromatic scale, can play the colors of the spectrum in any succession or combination, flashing on a screen all possible gradations of color, simultaneously or in any desired succession, producing at will the most delicate and subtle modulations of light and color, or the most gorgeous and startling contrasts and color chords! It seems to me that we have here at least as great a possibility of rendering all the fancies, moods, and emotions of the human mind as in the older art.

These beauties of form and color, so constantly recurring in the varied phenomena of refraction, diffraction, and interference, are, however, only incidentals; and, though a never-failing source of aesthetic delight, must be resolutely ignored if we would perceive the still higher beauties which appeal to the mind, not directly through the senses, but through the reasoning faculty; for what can surpass in beauty the wonderful adaptation of Nature's means to her ends, and the never-failing rule of law and order which governs even the most apparently irregular and complicated of her manifestations? These laws it is the object of the scientific investigator to discover and apply. In such successful investigation consists at once his keenest delight as well as his highest reward.[6]

Confident vision read the expanding scale and perspective as a challenge rather than an obstacle. With mounting speed, new territories were opened and scientific links discovered among seemingly disparate fields. Einstein and Minkovsky were among those who constructed a common fabric from hitherto separated territories of human understanding. It is evident that there are new ways in which to control the pace

[6] A. A. Michelson, *Light Waves and Their Uses* (Chicago: University of Chicago Press, 1907), p. 2.

and scale of changes. On the one hand, the continuing human explorations have to be interlocked and interconnected in a common legible structure. The new vistas of knowledge, the new powers of energy, the new complexity of relationships have to find a new level of ecological balance. An uninhibited will to fly will only lead us to the fate of Icarus. The twentieth century has to find the wisdom of Daedalus if it is to learn its own measure, map its direction, and set its ecological limits. To domesticate the tremendous forces will require new ordering principles geared to the continuous dynamic changes of scale. If the twentieth century offers a basically different human environment it does so primarily because of the rapid expansion and contraction of its scale. If we move from the individual to global interdependence or back from group conditions to individual happiness, so do we move continuously from the scale of our senses to the atomic scale of events to the cosmic scale of space travel.

7

ENVIRONMENT AS PROGRAMMED HAPPENING*

MARSHALL McLUHAN
Fordham University and the University of Toronto

I T HAS BEEN SAID that the present time offers us such immediate access to the entire range of cultures of other times that the architect can orchestrate different spaces, with their differing sensuous involvements, with the same freedom as the composer and the conductor. The architect can, in this electric age, modulate the forms of space of many other cultures much as the poet can shape his rhythms by free choice among a great diversity of words. T. S. Eliot's celebrated observations in *The Use of Poetry and the Use of Criticism* about the activity of the "auditory imagination" seem now to be relevant to the architect in his shaping of spatial form:

What I call the "auditory imagination" is the feeling for syllable and rhythm, penetrating far below the conscious levels of thought and feeling, invigorating every word; sinking to the most primitive and forgotten, returning to

* Some of the material in the present essay was used by the author in the Purves Memorial Lecture for 1967 sponsored by the American Institute of Architects. It is here published for the first time.

the origin and bringing something back, seeking the beginning and the end. It works through meanings, certainly, or not without meanings in the ordinary sense, and fuses the old and obliterated and the trite, the current, and the new and surprising, the most ancient and the most civilized mentality.[1]

To say that we live mythically today while continuing to think conventionally may help to draw attention to the technological gap in our ordinary experience. Electric technology, simply because it is all at once, is also discontinuous. It tends therefore to create exterior situations that have all the structural characteristics of the human unconscious. To the rational observer who seeks to find connectedness and uniformity in the spaces of his world, the new situation presents an extreme form of the irrational.

When the inner spaces of our lives go outward, the result is a structure like Habitat at Expo '67. This is a mosaic form of composite spaces which in effect presents an X ray of our entire culture. It is really very much like any page of the telegraph press during the past century. The mosaic of items on a newspaper page are connected only by the dateline above them. There is no other connection. The mosaic arrangement of multiple items of daily news creates not a picture of the world but an X ray in depth. A picture has a vanishing point related to a fixed position from which the picture is taken, but a mosaic, like a total field of energy or relationships, does not present the means for a point of view or a fixed position. It is an all-at-once or mythical structure in which beginning and middle and end are simultaneously present.

T. S. Eliot explained in his essay "Tradition and the Individual Talent" that all literature and art from Homer to the present constitutes a simultaneous order that is totally modi-

[1] London: Faber and Faber, 1933, pp. 118–19.

fied by the advent of any new work. A new work creates new space for itself and for all the preexisting space, yet this is quite different from shifting one's point of view. A point of view depends upon a pictorial space that is uniform and continuous and connected.

The Western world discovered visual or pictorial space when the phonetic alphabet was invented. The unique property of the phonetic alphabet as contrasted with all other forms of writing is its power to translate sounds into visual space. The resulting stress and prominence given to the visual sense above the other senses increasingly created for Western man an environment built on the visual assumptions of uniformity, continuity, and connectedness. Such spatial assumptions scarcely existed in cultures based on acoustic patterns, for example. What appears to us as the irrationality of the preliterate world is in fact the result of structuring forms on perfectly consistent auditory assumptions from which visual continuity and connectedness have been abstracted.

A century ago, in 1868, Claude Bernard, the French pioneer of interior medicine, was elected to the French Academy. His phrase *le milieu intérieur* came at the same time that the French Symbolists were inventing *le paysage intérieur*. This interior landscape, the successor to the external landscape of the Romantic poets, was deliberately programmed as a teaching machine, as it were, as appears in the very opening lines of Eliot's "Love Song of J. Alfred Prufrock":

> Let us go then, you and I,
> When the evening is spread out against the sky
> Like a patient etherised upon a table;

These lines wittily summarize both the first and second Romantic movements. The outer world of the setting sun is juxtaposed with the inner landscape of the patient's interior.

In his *Background of Modern Poetry* J. Isaacs has some relevant things to say about these two kinds of space. He considers them as two waves:

> . . . The first wave is a romantic notion, and belongs to the Pre-Romantic age of the middle of the eighteenth century, when poetry was sought in primitive poetry, in ancient poetry, in ballads and in archaic writing, much as modern art sought its inspiration in archaic sculpture and African carvings. The second wave is in the Symbolist movement of the end of the nineteenth century. If we like to attach names to the two waves, we can call them Ossian and Mallarmé. In both there is a striving beyond mere statement in order to gain a special effect. The earlier movement was a movement *against* something. The later was a movement *towards* something, and only incidentally against the moral and the didactic in poetry.[2]

The first movement is concerned mainly with Euclidean and Newtonian space. The second one takes us "through the looking glass" into the space-time world of modern physics. The first space is continuous and connected and uniform. It is a visual space. The second space is discontinuous and not uniform and not connected. It is auditory space or tactile space or kinetic or proprioceptive. As D. H. Lawrence wrote of it:

> Still, and sensitive, and active,
> Audile, tactile, sensitiveness as of a tendril which
>   orientates and reaches out,
> Reaching out and grasping by an instinct more delicate
>   than the moon's as she feels for the tides.

The first space is one that permits detachment and objectivity. The second kind demands empathy and involvement. The second Romantic movement naturally concentrated upon the *effect*.

[2] New York: E. P. Dutton & Co., 1952, p. 19.

As the Western world separates itself from a 2500-year devotion to visual space, it naturally rediscovers the characteristics of the spaces generated by the other senses. I vividly recall an occasion when I made my first encounter with acoustic space as a concept. Professor Jacqueline Tyrwhitt, now at the Harvard School of Design, was a member of our Toronto seminar on Culture and Communications. She had been explaining some of Siegfried Giedion's recent findings in which he discriminated between enclosed and unenclosed spaces. Since that time his study of *The Beginnings of Architecture* has brought these matters into a luminous focus. As Professor Tyrwhitt followed his exploration of Egyptian as contrasted with Roman space, she stressed the point that a pyramid did not enclose any space since darkness is to space what silence is to sound. In the same way, an Egyptian temple does not enclose space since it, too, is dark. Even the Greeks never achieved true closure of space. This remained for the Romans. At this point psychologist Carl Williams (now President of the University of Western Ontario) intervened. He observed that unenclosed space could best be considered as acoustic or auditory space. Williams had long been associated with E. A. Bott, who has spent his life studying auditory space. Bott's formula for auditory space is simply that it has no center and no margins since we hear from all directions simultaneously. Structurally, it tends to be the space of all preliterate societies since the auditory sense has much primacy over the visual sense in preliterate cultures.

Structurally, auditory space tends also to be the characteristic form of an electronic culture. Instant movement of information creates a configuration of space-time in which no point of view is possible and no single plane perceptible. Electronic configurations, in short, are in a structural sense remarkably acoustic. All-at-onceness abolishes uniformity and continuity, and it also demands that the environment will be considered as an art form. "We have no art," say the Balinese. "We do everything as well as possible." The instantaneous movement of information itself creates a total environment, as witness the satellites that now encompass the planet itself in an information environment. It is only the sense of sight that possesses the properties of uniformity and continuity and connectedness. And it is only in those cultures in which phonetic literacy is salient that we can find visual values of rational connectedness to be pervasive.

At the present time, therefore, the Western world, long based on visual values of rational continuity, finds itself cut adrift from these sensory ground rules. The electronic age, if given its own unheeded leeway, will drift quite naturally into Oriental modes of cosmic humanism and total involvement of everybody in everybody and of all spaces and all cultures converged into a kind of mosaic without walls. We have already moved into this dimension, and the resulting panic is to some degree compensated by enthusiasm for the disappearance of many of the barriers, private and corporate, that had been carefully erected by our visually oriented forebears.

This visual world is one of matching, of fragmentation, and of classification. The new multisensuous world is one of making in which space is not a cavity to be filled but a possibility to be shaped. Even when put in these terms the advantages seem to be all on the side of making rather than matching. However, in a tribal and amorphous world of interacting resonances, the discovery of new means to private identity and private space naturally appeared Utopian, as we can see from Plato's *Republic*. But the *Oedipus Rex* of Sophocles reports the inner terrors that accompanied that achievement of detribalizing man into private visual space.

We, too, experience similar terrors today as we go through the reverse process of retribalizing and of yielding up our private visual structures to the resonance of acoustic space. Our children are born into a total electric environment of information only to find themselves inserted into a very different kind of environment at school. Quite naturally, the educational establishment represents a blueprint of classified information and fragmented time that were designed to instruct by imprinting data and disciplines upon the growing child. That is to say that the educational establishment is a faithful reflex of visual culture.

In recent decades the establishment has become enveloped in a new information environment that causes a kind of reversal within. The new need is to direct the educational enterprise toward discovery rather than instruction. As the environment becomes richer in information than the classroom, the student's genuine role becomes diverted toward involvement and discovery rather than focused on the acquisition of classified data.

A similar reversal takes place in the business world. As the information environment gets richer and richer, job holding yields to role playing. A role tends to be created when several jobs converge. A surgeon has a role rather than a job, as does a top executive or a mother. Each of them has several jobs to perform simultaneously. An artist has a role rather than a job because he must use all his faculties at once.

In the older fragmented and mechanized world of specialisms we tended to use only a part of our faculties at any one time. This was called "work." When, like the artist, we use all our faculties at once, we are recognized to be playing and are at leisure. A man must work very hard at his hobby, but because he uses all his faculties when playing, he is thought to be at leisure.

The electronic information environment tends to create this new configuration of leisure via total involvement. Looked at in the rear-view mirror, this leisure takes on the illusory form of unemployment and joblessness and vacancy. In point of fact, leisure is a space-time dimension that must be shaped and created by the individual user. Such leisure is not a goal but a kind of total field of relations. It is nothing less than social communication. A child of the electronic age, looking around him at the job holders, cannot help but feel that they are pathetic holdovers from some other age. When a child assumes similar postures and activities he feels rejected and alienated.

The first and second Romantic movements illustrate the eighteenth-century discovery of the external environment as a natural teaching machine. This discovery was made possible by the advent of the new man-made environment of mechanical industry, just as the mechanical environment became an especial object of attention with the advent of the environment of electric information.

Any environment has the property of being mainly invisible. This is a theme of *The Hidden Dimension* by Edward T. Hall. His earlier study of time as *The Silent Language* is complementary to this new book on space. Whatever involves us or totally surrounds us acquires the property of being imperceptible. It has been observed that "we don't know who discovered water but we are pretty sure it wasn't a fish." Robert Ardrey has developed the concept of territoriality to account for the environments that envelop different cultures. My own concept of technologies as the physical extensions of man is somewhat akin to Ardrey's concept. However, it is easier to demonstrate the physical times and spaces created by radio or motor car than it is to explain why bird song or physical odor should constitute a space boundary that might be regarded as impenetrable by other creatures.

There are reasons why we should in our time have become aware of the environments created by ourselves. For one thing, the mere speed of change in these environments has made it possible to shift from one to another in such a way that discrimination by comparison and contrast becomes perfectly natural. Elias Canetti has written of *Crowds and*

Power, discussing the various structures and patterns of psychic space created by various types of crowds. For example, a football crowd has little in common with a symphony crowd. Most crowds are simply invisible except statistically. Yet statistics represent a new means of X-raying crowds of money and data which were impenetrable before the present age.

The same speed of access to many kinds of data has given us the power to X-ray all the cultures and subcultures in the world. We no longer approach them from any point of view or for the purpose of taking a picture of them. The new approach is the X-ray approach of penetration in depth to achieve awareness on many levels at once. It is natural that we should adapt this approach to our own condition. The psychiatrists have done so for the individual, and comparable analysis is now available for the corporate or group condition.

The habit of avoiding the present or the new which has been immemorial human tradition tends to yield to this X-ray approach of the structures that shape and surround human perception. *The Myth of the Eternal Return* by Mircea Eliade discusses in detail the age-old human habit of hiding from the present by cyclic images of repetition. Just as the ordinary person finds comfort in the repetitive routine of the daily round that prevents direct confrontation of the immediate situation, so have most preliterate societies, including the great cultures of Asia, protected themselves from pressures of the eternal present by assigning the entire show to a spinning mechanism.

The need for a rear-view mirror as preferable to direct confrontation is omnipresent in preliterate societies as much as in our own. In the same work, Eliade reports:

. . . Each time that life is threatened and the cosmos, in their eyes, is exhausted and empty, the Fijians feel the need for a return *in principio;* in other words they expect the regeneration of cosmic life not from its restoration but from its recreation. Hence the essential importance, in rituals and myths, of anything which can signify the "beginning," the original, the primordial (new vessels and "water drawn before sunrise" in popular magic and medicine, the motifs of the child, the orphan, and so forth).[3]

The perpetual presence of the dead in preliterate societies creates an abiding terror. They are the enemy, much as in our own world the artist is enemy because of his insistence that we look at the present. He is somewhat in the position of the small child at the exhibition of the Emperor's new clothes. The artist has little inclination to look at the old clothes and is fascinated by the new manifestations of form and sense.

In the present time, the artist has shifted his attention from the private to the corporate scene and space. A happening as a programmed art form expresses the need to deal with the total environment as a work of art or as what Daniel Boorstin would call "pseudo-event." In the age of electric information the service industries take over the total human environment as their responsibility: everything from government and education to entertainment networks is involved in creating "happenings," as it were, or in transforming the environment into a work of art. Town planners report that during the past thirty years more space has been enclosed architecturally than in the preceding six thousand years. The next thirty years will see a great escalation of this process. In other words, without even looking beyond architecture it is possible to see the world as a happening today.

Siegfried Giedion was one of the first to train perception in these matters. His book *Mechanization Takes Command* is subtitled *A Contribution to Anonymous History*. At the outset he mentions how a split had occurred between thought and feeling in the nineteenth century. This break had come about through mechanization. One could add that the gap

[3] *The Myth of the Eternal Return* (New York: Pantheon Books, 1954), p. 81.

between mechanical culture of the nineteenth century and the new organic and integral culture of the present electric age was also a means of making us aware both of the nature of the mechanical and of the nature of the electrical.

The mechanical proceeds by fragmentation of all processes, including the process of perception. The mechanical enthroned the "point of view," the static position, with its vanishing point. The electric age favors a total field approach, a kind of X ray of forms in depth which not only avoids a point of view but avoids looking at situations from any single level. Giedion's opening section on "Anonymous History" asserts the importance of this X-ray approach to the most ordinary forms:

> For the historian there are no banal things. Like the scientist, the historian does not take anything for granted. He has to see objects not as they appear to the daily user, but as the inventor saw them when they first took shape. He needs the unworn eyes of contemporaries, to whom they appeared marvelous or frightening. At the same time, he has to establish their constellations before and after, and thus establish their meaning.
>
> History writing is ever tied to the fragment. The known facts are often scattered broadcast, like stars across the firmament. It should not be assumed that they form a coherent body in the historical night. Consciously, then, we represent them as fragments, and do not hesitate, when necessary, to spring from one period to another. Pictures and words are but auxiliaries; the decisive step must be taken by the reader. In his mind the fragments of meaning here displayed should become alive in new and manifold relations.

This passage is a kind of manifesto of the mosaic approach that has supplanted the pictorial. For, paradoxically, pictures are opaque, whereas the mosaic lets light through in depth and transforms the entire environment of artifacts into a teaching machine. Perceptually, any environment whatever is a teaching machine in so far as it adjusts our sensory levels until they are accommodated to that environment. The "Anonymous History" approach, however, accepts the entire world as an organized happening that is charged with luminous and exciting messages. To read the language of forms, anything from a Cadillac to an ash tray renders the book of the world an inexhaustible source of insights and discoveries.

William Butler Yeats once observed that the emotion of multitude results in a poem or a play when more than one story line is present. When there is both a plot and a subplot, there is an effect of depth and richness out of all proportion to the components of the poem or play. Something like this seems to have happened to us on a planetary scale. When we put the man-made environment of the satellites around our planet, Nature itself becomes the content of a man-made environment.

The natural tendency when one environment goes inside another is for the contained to become an art form. While our electric technology tends to put the human unconscious outside as a sort of discontinuous, mythic environment of forms that coexist and are simultaneous, the putting of Nature inside a man-made satellite environment results in substituting our human rational responses for the old irrational nature. The human dialogue used to be carried on with Nature, as it were, and is now carried on with the man-made environment that has supplanted Nature. This situation puts artists and architects in a totally new role of making and generating values, where previously we had been spectators. Of course, we could be as deluded as the two fish in *The New Yorker* cartoon who were pictured as having climbed out of the water onto the shore. One says to the other: "This is where the action is!"

8

THE DOCTRINE OF CREATION AND HUMAN RESPONSIBILITY

JOHN MACQUARRIE
Union Theological Seminary

THE TITLE of this essay brings together two notions that are not perhaps very obviously related. One is a mythological or theological idea concerning the origins of the world. The other is the idea of the advance of man through the expansion of knowledge and through his growth in experience. The expression "education of the human race" is borrowed from the title of Lessing's famous work, and although we do not propose to discuss Lessing's specific views, the whole context of ideas lying behind this expression belongs typically to the Enlightenment and to the modern world that has emerged from it. When we attend to this, it becomes harder than ever to see how such a progressive, humanistic conception can be related to ancient stories of the creation. Of course, we often hear nowadays from some biblical theologians that the Judeo-Christian doctrine of creation, by abolishing the notion of an animistic universe, made possible the secularization of nature and so laid it open to scientific investigation. As we shall see, this is much too simple a statement of the relation between the doctrine of creation and the rise of modern knowledge, but there is a measure of truth in it. However, it would seem to suggest that the doctrine of creation, though it may have been important in the past in giving encouragement to the scientific enterprise, has served its purpose and is no longer of any more than historical interest. But I intend to argue in this essay that the doctrine of creation has a continuing importance for the education of the race. I do not think we want to fall back into the deism of former centuries—though some contemporary theologians seem to be in danger of this—and suppose that although God set things going in the beginning, he is now an absentee landlord who leaves us to manage as best we can.

Almost every race and religion have their stories of creation, but we shall concern ourselves only with the biblical doctrine. Creation is a pervasive idea of the Old Testament, for it meets us not only in the creation stories at the beginning of Genesis but also in the Psalms and in the writings of the prophets. The idea is taken over into the New Testament and is indeed used to interpret the distinctively Christian belief that God has acted decisively in Jesus Christ, for the result of this act is seen as a "new creation."[1]

We would go far wrong if we supposed that creation stories, whether those of the Bible or other ones, were concerned primarily with speculations about the beginnings of the world. Disinterested questions about the origins of the universe come only much later. Though the early stories of the creation do in fact tell how things began, their interest is obviously an existential one. They are not trying to answer the merely curious question of what happened in the beginning but are rather seeking to answer a question that lies much nearer to man and is much more urgent—the question of his own identity. We first begin to understand the creation stories when we see them as answers to the question: "Who are we?" To this extent, Bultmann's existential interpretation of mythology is justified. Regin Prenter is essentially correct

[1] II Cor. 5, 17.

in his judgment of the Old Testament witness to the creation: "The concern of the Old Testament is not to explain how the world came into existence; its concern is that the life of the world may be preserved."[2] There is striking confirmation of this point in the current situation, in which we now realize that the question of cosmic origins is an empirical one, to be decided by such techniques as radiotelescopy which reaches far into the past, and that this has nothing to do with the theological meaning of creation.

We are saying then that the doctrine of creation is to be understood primarily in existential or anthropological terms. It tries to answer man's question about himself, that is to say, to give him a self-understanding; and perhaps it could be argued that self-understanding or self-knowledge is both the most difficult and the most important item that goes into the education of the human race.

Yet the interpretation of the doctrine cannot remain narrowly existential or anthropological. Man does not exist as an isolated subject. He is always a being-in-the-world. Thus he is inseparable from his environment and unintelligible apart from it. He is, moreover, a social being, a being-with-others, so that he is to be understood also in a social context. But any society, in turn, lives within a history and can be understood only in the stream of history. But history belongs within a cosmos, and we find ourselves asking about its status and significance there. Is history the clue to the whole, or only a by-product? Where do these questions stop?

The answer is that we must carry them as far as we can go. Man is the ontological entity, whose very being leads him into the question of being. To understand himself, he must also try to understand the wider being within which his own specifically human being is set. And there are no limits that can be set to the questions he asks. In vain would the positi-

---

[2] *Creation and Redemption*, trans. by Theodor I. Jensen (Philadelphia: Fortress Press, 1966), p. 193.

vist erect barriers and ask man to be content with understanding himself as the cooking animal or the featherless
biped or whatever. So that although we say that the creation
stories have primarily an existential and anthropological
interest, this interest inevitably broadens out into an ontological and cosmological one. Yet this has to do not with
origins but with meaning, and any ontological or cosmological dimension of the stories (and of the doctrine based
on them) is inseparable from the existential interest.

These points are surely well established from a brief
examination of the two creation narratives at the beginning
of Genesis. Much the older of the two stories, the so-called
Yahwist account of creation, now stands second.[3] Its overwhelmingly anthropological interest is apparent. God first
of all makes man. Then he provides a background and environment for him, by planting the garden and by providing
in it such plants and animals as are useful to human life. In
this story, everything is seen from the human point of view
and any cosmological interest is strictly secondary to the
central interest of providing man with an identity and a self-
understanding. The later and much more sophisticated story
of creation from the source P, now standing first in the
biblical text,[4] is very different and in its ordered account of
the work of creation is remarkably similar to modern theories
of emergent evolution. First, God creates the light in a blind-
ing initial flash of energy. Then heaven and earth, land and
sea take shape, the vegetation and the animals appear, and
finally man himself is created. Here the cosmological interest
is much more pronounced, but the creation culminates in
man, and he is given dominion over the earth. So one can
still say that the story is designed to provide a self-understanding, but the self-understanding is less narrowly circum-
scribed, for to answer adequately the question of man is to

[3] Gen. 2, 4–25.
[4] Gen. 1, 1–2, 3.

be drawn into all the questions that man himself, as the ontological entity, raises.

What, then, is the self-understanding that is conveyed in the biblical stories of creation? In the Yahwist account, man is said to be constituted by the dust of the ground and the breath of life. Under these symbols, the basic tensions of human existence, in both its facticity and its possibility, come to expression. As dust of the ground, man understands himself in his solidarity with nature, in his finitude and earthiness. Yet as the bearer of breath or spirit, he has a unique place in creation. He is not just another item in the world of creatures but may be said even to transcend the world. He is tied to it and belongs within it, yet at the same time he rises above it and stands in an openness of possibility that is unique among the creatures. The same polarity appears in the later creation story. Man comes along at the end of the work of creation and is obviously part of the series. Again, his earthiness is fully recognized. But he alone is made in the "image" of God. Early Christian theologians tended to think of this "image" as man's rational nature. Man is the rational (*logikos*) being because he has a share in the divine Word (*Logos*), through whom the worlds were made. Modern scholarship would consider the emphasis on reason as too narrowly intellectualist a way of representing what is meant by the divine image in man. A more existential interpretation of the *imago Dei* is required, and perhaps we find it in the notion of the openness of the human existent, for it is this openness that lets him be transcendent and creative, and it is in these respects that the likeness to God manifests itself. But of course this understanding was present in the older theology also, because of the association of the *Logos* with creation. In any case, the mention of the divine image in the P account of creation and the subsequent command to man to subdue the earth marks him off as the creature with a unique status.

The biblical stories of creation are far from a dualistic account of man. Here they may be contrasted with Gnostic and Manichean myths, in which man is compounded of radically different and incompatible elements. While the Bible recognizes the polarities of human existence, it conceives these to be embraced within a unity. In spite of his uniqueness, man belongs within the world. He is not an angel or some spiritual being that has fallen away and become entangled in an alien matter. Yet it is just because the unity of man is asserted that the tensions within that unity present such an urgent problem. These tensions threaten to tear man apart: possibility in conflict with facticity, aspiration in conflict with impotence, rationality contradicted by irrationality, the freedom of spirit tied down to the fate of the dust. As man began to reflect and to question, there was no problem more urgent or more difficult than simply the problem of identifying himself.

These biblical writers expressed their solution to the problem in their use of the word "God." Although men's ways of thinking about God have varied greatly, I believe there is a constant strand of meaning expressed in the word. It is a far cry from the mythologically conceived God of whom one could use language like "walking in the garden in the cool of the day" to the subtle concepts of God that are current in twentieth-century philosophy and theology, and yet in the discourse of religion the word has fundamentally the same use. Schubert Ogden put the matter very well when he wrote: "I hold that the primary use or function of [the word] 'God' is to refer to the objective ground in reality itself of our ineradicable confidence in the final worth of our existence."[5] It is this use that has remained constant through the changing images of God. The word "God" is used to express faith in being—faith in human existence but also, beyond that, in the ontological context of our existence. When men say "God,"

[5] *The Reality of God* (New York: Harper & Row, 1966), p. 37.

they are affirming that in spite of its polarities and in spite of the distortions into which these polarities can push us, human existence does make sense. The opposite point of view, the denial of God, regards human existence as fundamentally absurd or senseless. We may, according to this view, be able to construct limited areas of meaning and value, but in the end, man is absurd in the universe. His uniqueness is the uniqueness of a freak, a wild accident. This view finds classic expression in Sartre's famous description of man as the "useless passion." This does not prevent Sartre or anyone else who shares his view from pursuing worthwhile ends, but there is a fundamental pessimism in it all. One may sometimes wonder whether (as Ogden suggests, and as writers such as John Baillie and Karl Rahner have also contended) the professed atheist who devotes himself to moral aspirations is not an implicit or anonymous believer. But for my part, I hesitate to say anything of the sort, for it might seem to place in doubt the very integrity of the man whose moral commitment is being admired.

The doctrine of creation, then, aims at providing man with a self-understanding. It brings him to understand himself in the fundamental polarities of his being and goes on to assert that these polarities are not to be interpreted as a senseless and frustrating dualism but that they make sense and provide man with the raw material, as it were, for a great destiny. How do we link this doctrine with the education of the human race, understood as man's growth in knowledge and experience?

I have already alluded to the view that the biblical doctrine of creation was a major factor in the encouragement of scientific investigation, though I also indicated that this is a limited thesis. The ancient Hebrews, after all, though they had a doctrine of creation, were hardly distinguished for their scientific or technical prowess. They were inferior in war to their neighbors who had iron chariots, and in the arts of peacetime they had to call in foreigners for such projects as the building of the Temple. Christianity all but smothered the incipient science of Greece. Aristotle's accurate descriptions of animals were replaced by the medieval bestiaries, which were interested more in spinning out the alleged moral and spiritual "significations" of the animals than in giving information about their observable characteristics. There follows the sad story of the Church's repeated clashes with the men of science, astronomers, geologists, and biologists in turn. This opposition between the men of biblical faith and the men of science was not merely accidental, though contemporary theologians try to forget it. There is certainly no simple explanation of the immensely complex rootage of the Western scientific outlook, as those who have tried to write the history of the West have shown.

But if we avoid exaggerations, we can nevertheless acknowledge that the biblical doctrine of creation made its contribution. However, there are different opinions on how this contribution was made. There seem to be at least four ways of understanding it.

1. The first way focuses on man's special status in the scheme of creation and on the command to him that he should subdue the earth. This self-understanding contains within itself the drive toward the exploration and utilization of the earth's resources. Man becomes aware that he is not just a part of nature but has a unique power and dignity through which he can bring the earth and the phenomena of nature more and more under his control and more and more into his service. If one were to use the contemporary terminology of Teilhard de Chardin, one could say that, on this first view of the matter, the creation doctrine expresses the idea of "hominization." Within the created sequence there appears a being who, although belonging to that sequence, nevertheless transcends it in such a way that the control of the world, hitherto vested in impersonal laws of nature, is now being

transferred to the personal being who stands out from the world. Man stands out from the blind and passive system of nature as the transcending being in whom nature has become self-conscious and self-directing, so that even if one can still speak of a human "nature," one has to acknowledge that this nature has acquired an openness that does not belong to nature below the human level. Perhaps one could express precisely the same idea by saying that the biblical doctrine of creation points to the contrast between nature and history. Man does not have his being as part of a natural process but as one who makes and is made by history. It is well known, of course, that the biblical stories of creation were not unconnected with the Hebrew experience of history, and this indeed was implied in our earlier contention that the interest of these stories is anthropological rather than cosmological. In the words of Walther Eichrodt, "there was a deliberate linking up of creation with history."[6] One may contrast this view of man, which takes him out of nature and places him in history, with the Greek understanding of him as part of the cosmos. Yet even to say this is to be reminded of the complexity of these problems and of the inadequacy of any simple or one-sided answers, for it was the Greeks who advanced much further in science than ever the Hebrews did.

2. A second way of looking at the relation between the doctrine of creation and the rise of science stresses rather the profane character of the world. In pantheism, the world itself is divine; in polytheism, many beings within the world are either divine or demonic. So man feels himself inhibited in his handling of the world, and we all know how, in various countries, ancient superstitions can have a very oppressive effect on the people and may hinder the use and development of scientific methods in medicine, agriculture, and other fields. But in a doctrine of creation, the world is external to

[6] *Theology of the Old Testament,* trans. by J. A. Baker (London: Student Christian Movement Press, 1961), I, 231.

the Creator. God has become transcendent, and the world itself is cleared of divinity and left open to exploitation for the sake of man. The argument is well summarized by an eminent physicist of our time, Carl von Weizsäcker, who has himself been influenced by the Protestant theologian, Friedrich Gogarten:

> The gods of nature have been vanquished by the God whom Christians call "Our Father." Therefore man, as God's son, has received power over nature. As he is son, and not servant, he is free, and his freedom includes the freedom to act against the will of the Father, the God of love. He can now subject the world to himself, and secularism does precisely this.[7]

The last two sentences of the quotation, however, make it clear that the author considers the secular scientific outlook to have a decidedly ambivalent character, and to this we must return.

3. I must now draw attention to a somewhat different reading of the situation, found, for instance, in Karl Jaspers, and this reading is not easily harmonized with the one just expounded. On this third view, the stress is upon the dignity and worth of the world rather than on its profane character. God made the world and pronounced it to be good. It is therefore a worthy object on which man can bestow his thought and work. To say that the world is made by God and is therefore good separates the biblical doctrine of creation from all Manichean and dualistic views, according to which the material universe is essentially evil. If the physical universe is considered evil, then indeed there would be little incentive to scientific investigation. But something of this dualism was present in the Hellenic understanding of the world. Greek science failed to develop further than it did not because it lacked theoretical foundations but because it was not sufficiently empirical. The Greek scientist did not want to soil his

---

[7] *The Relevance of Science* (London: Collins, 1964), p. 178.

hands, so to speak, by getting immersed in experiments, so he dealt with the ideal objects of the mind. (This is a generalization to which there are obvious exceptions, such as Aristotle's observations of animals, mentioned above.) But when the world was understood as God's creation, it acquired a new dignity and the way was opened for empirical science. The point is perhaps best illustrated by contrasting Greek physics with modern physics.

4. There is still another way of looking at the matter. We mentioned that when they introduce the word "God," the old creation stories are declaring their fundamental faith that man's being-in-the-world makes sense. Although we thought of this primarily from the anthropological point of view, it clearly implies that the world makes sense, as does man's existence, as well. There is a *Logos* in the world as well as a *Logos* in man. Only the confidence that there is an order in the world could sustain the endeavor to discover this order. This faith in the orderliness of the world was called "cosmic religion" by one of the greatest scientists of modern times, Albert Einstein. "The most incomprehensible thing about the world," he declared, "is that it is comprehensible."[8] Einstein moreover thought of this "cosmic religion" as standing in historical continuity with the Old Testament.

But is all this merely of historical interest? Does it show that, among many other factors, the doctrine of creation contributed toward the rise of scientific inquiry in the West but that we have now outgrown that doctrine? It encouraged man to seek knowledge of natural phenomena, and this knowledge in turn allowed him to gain control over them. But now that man has taken over, is the doctrine of creation still of any significance or has it served its purpose?

Many writers who acknowledge the usefulness of the doctrine of creation in the Western tradition do in fact seem to think that this usefulness belonged only to the past and

[8] *Albert Einstein: Philosopher Scientist,* P. A. Schlipp, ed. (New York: Harper & Row, 1959), I, 248.

that today the doctrine is effete. But we have made it clear at the beginning of this essay that our own conclusion would be different and that we would try to show that the doctrine of creation has a continuing importance for the education of the human race.

A pointer in the direction in which we wish to move was already given when we noted Carl von Weizsäcker's reservations about the ambivalence of secularization and the rise of science. Actually, in the four points outlined above, we have presented a somewhat one-sided interpretation of the biblical material. Certainly, in the Bible, the shift from nature to history is not intended to eliminate God from the picture, for although history is constituted by man's free choices, it is still supposed to be under the providential control of God; and the history of the Old Testament is presented as the story of God's dealings with his people and the fulfilling of his purposes for them. So we have here something much more complex than simply a contrast between heteronomy and autonomy. It is not a question of a disjunction between man's being part of a cosmic system and his exercising an unrestricted freedom. Rather, the kind of history envisaged in the Bible implies a dialectical relationship between the freedom of man and the providence of God; or, to express this differently, man's freedom is set in a context of grace and judgment. But this dialectic is implicit also in the manner in which man is presented in the creation stories, for it is again one-sided to dwell on his transcendence of the world and to forget that he is also part of it. While man is indeed said to be made in the image of God, he is quite definitely assigned to the creation, and there is no merging of the human into the divine, in Hebrew thought, as there is in the classical conceptions of demigods and heroes. Indeed, in the story of the fall of man, it is the desire to be as God that is represented as his undoing.

These biblical ideas, I would claim, are not simply old-fashioned remnants of the creation story which can now be dispensed with. They belong integrally to that self-understanding that found expression in the creation narratives, and we go wrong if we think that the import of these stories for modern man is to be seen only in the handing over of the world to man for his exploitation.

The important point that has also to be borne in mind is that man's freedom is not an absolute, and that his position in the world is not that of absolute sovereign but rather that of steward. One contemporary philosopher who has expressed very clearly in the context of a secular philosophy what is the essence of the biblical insight is Martin Heidegger, who writes in one place: "Man is not the lord of beings; he is the guardian of Being."[9]

Man then is considered the steward or guardian of Being. Perhaps the word that best expresses his relation to the world in which he finds himself is "responsibility." He does not have the world at his absolute disposal but is made responsible for it. The terrible danger of the technological age, as already hinted at by Carl von Weizsäcker, is that it may become dominated by the subjective will-to-power. But man, who is creaturely as well as self-transcending, must learn to understand himself as freely cooperating in an enterprise much bigger than he knows about. He has to handle the creation and make use of its resources with responsibility—not only a responsibility toward other men, of his own generation and of generations to come, but a responsibility toward the cosmos as a whole, and a responsibility toward the mysterious creative source whom we call God. The development of such a sense of responsibility is surely one of the most urgent needs in the further education of the human race, and the biblical doctrine of creation is very relevant in helping us toward such a self-understanding. A doctrine of responsibility is a

9 *Über den Humanismus* (Frankfurt-am-Main: Vittorio Klostermann, 1947), p. 19.

reminder that there are no rights without corresponding duties and that talk about the rights of man must be correlated with an understanding of his obligations. Perhaps it is no accident that at this very time the idea of responsibility is apparently assuming a more important role in Christian thought. This idea is obviously a key one in the contemporary Catholic moral theology of Bernard Häring; while among Protestant thinkers, Fritz Buri makes the idea of responsibility central in his theological exposition. A responsible self-understanding is a major need of our contemporary world, and it may well be asked whether such responsibility can maintain itself apart from that vision of man and the world which found its classic expression in the biblical doctrine of creation.

II

AREAS OF KNOWLEDGE

9

THE SPIRIT OF SCIENCE AND
MORAL INVOLVEMENT

JERROLD R. ZACHARIAS
Massachusetts Institute of Technology

T HE EDUCATIONAL POLICIES COMMISSION of the
National Education Association published, in 1966,
a booklet called *Education and the Spirit of Science*.[1] I read
it eagerly, because for many years I have found it so hard to
explain what is the spirit of science to someone who is not
himself a scientist or who has not spent many years in a
science laboratory or working with scientific theory.

It was, however, this very difficulty that aroused my
objections. As I wrote to I. I. Rabi, a member of the Commission and one of my oldest friends, who had sent me a
copy:

> Thank you for sending me *Education and the Spirit of
> Science*; I am very glad to have it. Surely it was written
> by someone whose heart is on the right side of the issues,
> but the account itself I consider to be repetitious and
> mushy. It is hard for me to believe that it would be un-
> derstandable to anyone who was not already convinced by
> his own experience. . . .
>
> I will try to send along some specifics in a few days,

[1] Washington, D.C.: Educational Policies Commission, National
Education Association of the United States, 1966.

[141]

specifics which might make the spirit of science more comprehensible.

My reactions were aimed primarily at a list of values "on which science is everywhere based" and that "characterize the enterprise of science as a whole." As cited in *Education and the Spirit of Science*, they are:

1. Longing to know and to understand
2. Questioning of all things
3. Search for data and their meaning
4. Demand for verification
5. Respect for logic
6. Consideration of premises
7. Consideration of consequences[2]

I have no objection to these statements, except insofar as I believe that one cannot understand them unless one has in mind specific examples. I believe that professional scientists, while they are exercising their profession as scientists, always work from specific examples, however simple or complex, to the awesome generality. And I believe that the only way to clarify this notion is for me to wallow in some specific examples so that you know what the discussion is about.

Longing to know and to understand. The spirit of science . . . seeks to understand because it accepts knowledge as desirable in itself. It expresses its curiosity endlessly, recognizing that questions are infinite, answers finite.[3]

What bothers me about this is simple. I do not believe that longing to know or understand is unique with science or scientists. Man is surrounded by an endless amount of mystery. And those of us who work in science content ourselves with trying to understand only a small part of this infinite mystery.

Let me give a specific example. Several years ago at the

[2] *Ibid.*, p. 15.
[3] *Ibid.*, p. 17.

beginning of the Kennedy Administration, the members of the President's Science Advisory Committee were discussing the advisability of endorsing a program to put a man on the moon. I was very much opposed to it. I thought that the expenditure of billions of dollars for that project would make the public content that it was indeed supporting science. But having a man on the moon is only a very, very small part of what we hope to achieve scientifically in this century.

Finally it occurred to me that once we had satellites surrounding the earth, the public, including the scientific public, would become more curious about the physical laws that govern the behavior of a satellite. I remember thinking with pleasure that someday we would have, twenty-three thousand miles above a point on the earth's surface, a satellite that would be used as a transmitter and retransmitter of television and radio. People would wonder how man could put an object into space and hold it stationary with respect to us, without a skyhook, defying the law of gravity, and not falling into us.

The public, however, has not been aroused. To be sure, they are interested in the television and other communications that are transmitted and retransmitted. But Isaac Newton's very simple laws of motion, which explain how an object can remain poised as do the satellites, never seems to have affected the public, or even in fact the scientific public, except those people who happen to be interested in satellites or who need an example to teach a certain area of physics.

Why are so few people, with that supposed "longing to know and to understand," interested in an explanation of why the satellite stays there? I satisfy myself with a hypothesis pretty much as follows: a man is so accustomed to an infinite amount of mystery that understanding one little piece doesn't change that infinity at all. It's the nature of infinity that subtracting or adding doesn't change it.

My statement, then, about "longing to know and to understand" is that those of us who are professional scientists feel that just the experience of understanding, even though it be about something seemingly trivial, something simple, something not very deep, is enough to content us momentarily. We feel that one has to understand something simple in order to learn the nature of understanding itself. So we are content with some piece of understanding, whether or not it affects our entire structured understanding of everything. We feel it is better to understand something than to understand nothing, even though we cannot understand everything, or even very much.

> *Questioning of all things. Search for data and their meaning. Demand for verification.* 'There is no perfect knowledge and no perfect knower. Certainty, as a concept, is replaced by probability. All conclusions and decisions are more or less suspect; science rides on a preference for the less over the more.[4]

Again using examples, let me elaborate on certainty versus probability. I believe that the air I breathe, which is a mixture of gases, consists of molecules that are relatively far from one another, say ten molecule-diameters apart. They are as far apart as two people in a theater with ten seats between. And if you consider a theater so sparsely populated, a gas is not a very condensed substance.

One gets a little better feel for this if one condenses a gas. Whether nitrogen, oxygen, water vapor, or carbon dioxide is condensed into a liquid or a solid, the density changes by about a thousand. This means that the gas molecules are juxtaposed by a factor of about ten. The reason that the density is increased by a thousand, not ten, is that there are three dimensions. There are ten empty seats to the right and left, ten empty seats forth and back, and ten empty seats up and down. And ten times ten times ten is a thousand.

I further believe that these molecules in the gas of the air around us are moving roughly at the velocity of sound in air,

4 *Ibid.*, p. 17.

a thousand feet a second, or about thirty times as fast as a man can run. Going at all kinds of velocities in the neighborhood of this velocity—some faster, some slower—these molecules collide with one another and with the walls of the vessel and then bounce back. When they hit, they push on the wall, and the wall has to push on them to make them bounce back. It's turn and turnabout. The faster they move, the more momentum they carry; the heavier they are, the harder they push; and the harder they push on the wall, the harder the wall has to push back. The whole notion of gas as consisting of a chaotic collection of particles can be set up mathematically into what is known as the *kinetic theory of gases.*

If I ask students why they believe the kinetic theory of gases, they say, "It works, doesn't it?" or "It's accepted theory." And I say, "Yes, but on what experimental bases? How do you know? Why do you believe it? What's there?"

And we start. We start with some simple gas law such as, "The pressure of the gas times its volume is equal to the amount of gas and to its temperature (PV=NRT)." The hotter the temperature, everything else remaining constant, the higher will be the pressure. Everyone knows this. Just measure the pressure in your tires after driving at the speed limit on a hot summer day. Compare it with the pressure in that same tire before it's heated and after, to check.

In the equation PV=NRT, N is a measure of the amount of gas; T is the temperature; and R is a proportionality constant which, when measured for any gas, turns out to be 2 calories per gram molecular weight, or per *mole*. It's the same for all gases—already a miracle! You can measure this no matter what the gas—carbon dioxide, H_2O, H_2, argon, neon, and so on—and you keep getting the same constant, R, or 2 calories per mole.

For an entirely different kind of measurement, measure the amount of heat necessary to increase the temperature of a gas by 1° centigrade. Gas is an elusive thing. One can measure the amount of heat required to increase its temperature by holding its volume constant in a container that will not expand as the temperature rises, or one can try a similar experiment in an ordinary room in which the gas is free to expand so that its pressure, rather than its volume, remains constant. Obviously, in such experiments one must keep either the pressure or the volume constant.

Thus, the professionals have come to work with specific heat at constant volume, C_v, and specific heat at constant pressure, C_p. One can also measure the difference between C_v and C_p and lo and behold! what appears is that constant 2 calories per mole, the same constant, the same number for any gas, despite entirely different kinds of measurement.

Gases do more things. They are viscous; they resist the motion of something. For instance, the water droplets of a cloud are continually falling, but they're falling very slowly because of the viscosity of the air. Watch smoke coming out of a chimney, even on the most windless day. There it hangs. It has been going up because it was hot. But by the time it cools off, it just hangs in the air. It doesn't really "hang"; it is falling But it is falling slowly because of the viscosity of the air.

The kinetic theory of gases predicts that the viscosity of a gas is independent of pressure or density. For instance, if the air at high altitude, where the atmospheric pressure is low, were at the same temperature as sea level, smoke would fall at the same rate at high altitudes as at low. Your intuition would say that the denser the fluid through which the droplets fell, the more resistance there would be to the motion of the drops. What the theory predicts and what experiments support is against your intuition. If one measures the velocity of fall of smoke at pressure of one atmosphere, half an atmosphere, or a tenth of an atmosphere, the rate of fall is exactly the same in accordance with theory.

The theory predicts something else that is intuitively backward: as a gas becomes hotter, the viscosity gets higher rather than lower. Whereas your automobile engine is harder to start at lower temperature, because oil becomes more viscous, the opposite is true of gas. The kinetic theory predicts that the viscosity of a gas gets higher with higher temperature. I could provide all sorts of detailed support from actual measurements and actual observations. You can see that things fall at the same rate; you can see that something is more or less viscous without a lot of fancy measurements. Whenever you do this, the kinetic theory of gases is borne out.

For me, the molecular notion of a gas is a deep conviction. It is so deep that I don't feel that it can be just a probability. My conviction is so strong that I would bet everything I own, have, or could get on its veracity.

You might say, "That's a safe bet. What else could it be?" Well, just feel the air around you. Does it feel like a bunch of molecules colliding with you? Doesn't it feel rather like some kind of continuous, gauzy, vaporous, structureless, expansible fluid? After all, you can pour a heavy gas into a light gas. Gas does have many of the properties of fluids. But no one has ever found any evidence that disagrees with the kinetic theory of gases or any predictions that have not been verified.

That is the nature of a deep conviction. Not all notions in science have that particular depth. I've picked that specific one because to break or to overthrow it would require changing the results of already performed experiments that indicate that this belief is correct. This conviction is so deep that I would be willing to call it absolute, contrary to the caveats of *Education and the Spirit of Science.*

To be sure, there are some theories about which my conviction is considerably less solid. So let's go to the opposite extreme.

Astronomers often state that the distant galaxies beyond

ours are retreating from us with velocities that are proportional to their distances from us. This sounds incredible at first. It gives the feeling that we must be at the center of something. That is not, however, a necessary consequence. Imagine, for instance, that you are inside a large assemblage of things and that the whole assemblage is expanding. Then everything would be moving away from you, no matter which member of the group you were.

The theory of the behavior of galaxies goes even further. It says that the farther away the galaxy, the faster it is moving. We don't have much evidence for this. There is some in the form of the spectra of some of the atoms, which we believe are like atoms here on earth. The spectra of those atoms are shifted toward the red, indicating that their wavelengths are longer or their frequencies are less. And this can be interpreted as an indication that they are moving away from us. But the lack of much additional evidence leaves a weak belief.

When I suggested to a friend how improbable it is that the galaxies are moving away from us at speeds proportional to their distances away, he countered, "How would you like to have them? Fixed? Is that any more probable? Does that satisfy you any more?" I admitted that it did not.

But its still a weak belief, and if some notion came along such as the peculiarities of the space between us and the galaxies, I would not be surprised.

Respect for logic. Consideration of premises. Logic is the science of valid inference.[5]

Let me get to basic difficulties here right away. When all of us were younger and in secondary school we learned about a logical structure with Euclid. Euclid set up axioms and ways of operating with these axioms which resulted in theorems.

I remember how strange it was to go through a page or

[5] *Ibid.*, p. 19.

so of proof of something that seemed perfectly obvious. I remember explicitly one theorem that we were supposed to prove: *If you consider a point remote from a circle and draw two tangent lines from the point to the circle, the lengths of those tangent lines from the point to their tangency are equal.*

I don't remember the proof anymore, but I do remember my reaction: that it was a silly thing to do, to go through a lot of equations to prove something that was obvious. That object with the two tangent lines was symmetrical: all you had to do was turn it over. You couldn't say which tangent line was which; therefore, they must be equal.

I've confronted mathematicians subsequently with this very fundamental objection of a child to the nature of Euclid. They say very simply that the notion of using symmetry to prove something of this sort is powerful, clean, clear, and useful. But Euclid's axioms in this case were restricted to a plane. He could not invoke symmetry; he could not turn something over because he could not get out of plane. By turning something over, even in your head, you are getting out of the plane.

Logic, in other words, can be very constraining. So we must be sure to use not just *restrictive* formulations of logical representations of nature, but we must use formulations as *general* as man can think of. Not just for shortcuts, but because we have no sureness that our intuitive notions, which would help us set up our axiomatic system, are the right ones.

For an example I shall pick special relativity. Everyone is accustomed to thinking of space as space and time as time. They are not in the least confusable. Who would ever dream of measuring how far it is from here to there with a watch, or measuring how much time has passed by measuring the distance? Our intuitive notions are really straight on this. The only trouble is that they are wrong.

Even to define a space or a time, one has to use notions of simultaneity. When two simultaneous events are at the same

point in space—right at the observer—simultaneity is simple
to state and to understand. Consider, however, two events
like a flash of lightning ten miles away and a flash of lightning one mile away. The signals, the flashes of lightning,
take time to get to us. And so, if you ask, "Were the two
lightning bolts simultaneous?" the answer depends on where
the observer is. If the observer is halfway between the two
lightning flashes, he might see them at the same time. But
if he's off to either side, he sees them at different times. So
simultaneity itself is relative and depends on space.

Now the reason I go into all these particulars of this particular point is that logic with people who work with nature is
only partial. We live with a great many half-baked notions.
Even our "logical" notions of space and time are half-baked.
So the sentence, "Logic is the science of valid inference,"
leaves out that whole and most important notion that for the
study of nature logic is a very "iffy" business.

> *Consideration of consequences.* Awareness of implications
> can, like the rest of knowledge, at best be incomplete. But
> a rational person does not accept a value or decide upon
> action without trying to be aware of its implications.[6]

It is so tempting to believe that a physicist should be
selfless and valueless, that he should not make moral judgments because he cannot substantiate moral judgments in the
same scientific way that he validates his belief in simple and
direct affairs of nature. But there is more than this. A professional scientist lives an ethical life, in the science at least,
for a very simple reason. If he were to publish something
that he thought was not correct, he would know perfectly
well that his conclusions would not last long. Nor would his
reputation last long with his fellows.

It bothers me very much indeed that C. P. Snow, who
claims to have been a physicist, has written a novel in which

6 *Ibid.*, pp. 20–21.

the leading character, a physicist, falsifies some photographs. It just doesn't happen, except in those peculiar cases when the man becomes no longer a scientist but insane. There have been several cases in the last century of professional scientists who have gone out of their minds. And in a couple of those instances they falsified data.

Once more I cite an example. A few years ago, when scientists in the Soviet Union took photographs of the backside of the moon and distributed them to the world, a friend asked me, "Are they not just possibly faking? After all, none of us knows what the other side of the moon looks like. Couldn't they just say they went there and then send us a photograph?"

I laughed and said, "No. They may be Russians, but they are scientists. And they know they can't fake. It would hurt them if they did; it would hurt their souls."

At this point, instead of talking about moral consequences, I am switching to the education of children. I believe one can let children learn science, not only for its own sake, but also as a way to develop intellectual strength, intellectual integrity, and intellectual agility.

There are two questions here: (1) Is it possible to bring up children in a way so that they do not fall prey to dogmatism? (2) Besides listening to the precepts, guidance, knowledge, and prejudgments of their elders, can they understand —in their "guts," not just in their heads—that it is possible to learn about evidence by working with nature?

The nature with which they work must be uncomplicated enough, repeatable enough, simple enough, manageable enough, so that the children can close an experience within a finite number of weeks. If one takes the behavior of human beings as the subject on which to operate, the natural perversity of people who are sensitive to being watched makes it very difficult to find a clear piece of sociological data, uncolored by the reactions of the observed.

Two or three years ago in a meeting devoted to a study of medical education, one surgeon pointed out that psychiatry was so difficult because human beings are not predictable. I said, "Nonsense. It's just that we believe that what is predictable is trivial. For instance, I predict with almost complete certainty that of the forty people at this meeting, no one will appear naked at the breakfast tomorrow." Quick as a flash, two psychiatrists retorted, "Don't make the stakes too high."

On the other hand, let us look at how Roger Payne handled a study of seedlings with a class of elementary school children while he was developing a science unit for Educational Services Incorporated. The children had viewed a time-lapse film that showed bean seedlings raising and lowering their leaves in time with the day-night, darkness-light cycle. An observation that the plants grew upward rather than at an angle led to a discussion of whether or not a plant needed light to decide which way to grow. This question brought others and finally a decision to experiment with seeds, which the children themselves planted in varying conditions of light. Light from varying angles, absence of light, and light in different colors were tried on oat seeds planted in all sorts of containers. The teacher did not need to know any answers. In fact the children were better off and happier if the teacher professed ignorance and let them learn directly from the plants—from the stuff of nature itself. And their observations raised more questions—about the effects of gravity, temperature, moisture, and so on—questions the children themselves asked and sought answers to.

One aspect of science is that every time you ask a question, you almost always raise more questions than you answer. Science, then, is not an endless frontier but an expanding frontier. The more we understand, the more we see the tenuous nature of our innocent assumptions, as I mentioned before in talking about space and time.

Now I think I'm ready to say why I think science—not as a discipline but as something you've been brought up in, "a way of life"—has something to do with moral values. Let us use an example that strikes close to home. Some ten or fifteen years ago I was in a smoking compartment of a Pullman car, talking to a friend about control of atomic weapons. Rather casually I asked, "How many deaths and casualties do you think the United States could stand and still survive? As many as a few million? Or could we stand the slaughter of even twenty million?"

A man who seemed to be asleep sitting near us jumped to attention. "My God!" he exclaimed. "Do you realize you are talking about the possible extermination of 10 percent of the population of the country?"

I looked him squarely in the eye—he was still a bit shocked—and said, "No, sir. We're probably talking about the extermination of all of it, and every other man, too. One has to figure out where the limit would be."

The purpose of saying this kind of shocking thing here— and it shocks me, too, if only because it is possible to say— is to indicate the kind of person who has lived a life of trying to obey the Ten Commandments. So long as the world is in such a condition as to make it almost impossible to live by any particular moral law or precept, we must regard morality and the study of it as a living subject, just as alive as the forefront of any intellectual activity we engage in.

Why do I believe that living a life associated with scientific attitudes is beneficial to the understanding of moral issues, to trying to formulate moral principles? I guess it's because it comes natural for someone brought up with scientific attitudes to reject dogma or at least to look at dogma with a skeptical eye. Every time some scientific idea is taken for granted, we find we have to look further. Sometimes the agreement between nature and the dogmatic formulation is far from satisfactory. So naturally those of us who are professional scientists look at moral values in much the same way.

A few years ago I was one of many people who were frightened when the antipolio vaccine of Jonas Salk was introduced to the public in a wholesale way. I would have been more content to have taken our chances with the introduction of this radical vaccine to some fraction of the population. Validating a vaccine or medication of any sort does not require a sample as large as the total population. Ten or 20 percent of the population—a large sample—would have been enough. But polio is such a dreadful disease that it seemed to a great many professional physicians that the country was not taking too big a risk. Delaying the general application of the vaccine long enough to evaluate it fully would almost certainly have cost the lives of potential polio victims. Some group of people had to make a value judgment. They had to take their chances, and they took them with their eyes wide open.

It was a success story, but it need not have been. And what would we have thought then? "Those hard-boiled professional scientists don't care about human life." But it was exactly about human life that they were caring. It took a tremendous lot of thought, investigation, and weighing of evidence in order to reach a conclusion.

The method of handling large issues demands very careful weighing of all sorts of evidence, weighing one man's evaluation of human life against another's. Take, for instance, the now controversial issue of the bombing of North Vietnam. Many people have studied the problem of the bombing of the North, or they've studied the reasons for our involvement in Vietnam. But I have never heard of a study of this problem in which the primary aim was to determine the *moral* issues.

I propose that we go at moral issues explicitly but in a very substantive way. I believe that one doesn't understand moral issues without saying that moral issues are what you are going to work on. I am not saying that you can understand the moral problems in the Vietnam War without understanding the war itself, why we are there, what the involvement of other countries might or might not be, or what our emotional reactions to communism are or should be. One cannot separate his actions from practical issues. Moral judgments that are independent of practical issues are most likely to be unsound.

Every time scientists pull together groups that are man enough, strong enough, diverse enough, committed enough, and willing to spend time enough to understand something, we advance understanding. Sometimes we come to a very sharp decision and act on that. A scientist is explicit; he doesn't merely listen to somebody's statement. Those of us involved in science know perfectly well that every idea, no matter how simple sounding, is in fact very complex. It takes a lot of thought and study. And moral issues deserve just as much care as scientific issues.

Someone will reply, "But moral issues have been studied over the centuries by all sorts of extraordinary people. Take St. Augustine, or this man, or that man. . . ." The world is different now. They did not have atom bombs to worry about, or biological warfare, or machine guns, or the population density that we have, with its broken families or its particular form of racial violence and oppression, and so on and so on. It all has to be done again, and it will have to be done over again. One has to *continue* to do it to keep morality a living subject, as science is.

There is no special magic to the method of science. There is, however, a strange kind of humility that states simply, "Pay only small heed to the dogma; just remember that every question is more difficult than you think."

When do you make a decision on a moral issue? Anytime; you *constantly* have to make decisions. At what point do you know? There is no sharp way. A scientist decides to "finish" an experiment when additional time doesn't change the values very much. He says, "I could improve this with another two weeks or so, but I wouldn't improve it very much. In fact, it might go downhill." And when you're dealing with a moral issue, you say, "We have gone just about as far as we can go in our thinking, and now we must act." It's a good question: How do you know when to stop?

10

BIOLOGY AND HUMAN VALUES

JOHN T. EDSALL

Harvard University

The Inherent Values of Science

T HE PURSUIT OF SCIENCE, considered as the search for
the deepest possible understanding of the universe and
all that it contains, represents one of the supreme values of
life in our civilization. In an era so filled with turmoil,
hostility, and destruction as ours, such achievements as the
development of quantum mechanics and the unraveling of
the genetic code are among the few events of the modern
world of which our descendants may be unreservedly proud.
A deep appreciation of the value of science as such does
indeed require prolonged and arduous discipline; the value of
a deeper insight into the world, for the sake of the illumination that insight brings, is acknowledged by many but fully
appreciated by relatively few.

Science today, as a body of coherent knowledge, is certainly
one of the supreme creations of man. It differs from all, or
nearly all, of the great intellectual constructions of the past in
being coherent yet tentative, based in experimental fact but
subject always to modification by new discoveries. There are
branches of science that for many of us have a profound
aesthetic appeal, comparable to that of the greatest works of
art. I remember when, after many painful struggles as a

learner, I began to master the fundamental concepts of thermodynamics and to see the power of their application to solving vast numbers of special problems by the guiding light of a few great principles. It was like the vision one attains from the top of a great mountain after an arduous climb, an abiding vision that no one who has experienced it will forget, though he may forget all the details of what he has learned. But science is also messy and confused; it is full of unexplained, puzzling bits of information that do not yet fit into any coherent scheme; of experiments that go wrong, and of constant alternations of discouragement and elation for the investigator. No scientist today, even after a lifetime of devotion to the subject, can clearly see more than a few corners of its vast structure. Indeed it is no static structure but a growing organism, growing indeed at present with fabulous speed and extending pseudopodia in all directions.

This slightly grotesque image, however, scarcely does justice to the beauty of the subject or to its appeal and fascination for the scientist. The broad vistas of science are for me, as I think they are for many others, a constant source of inspiration. Whether one's own work is going well or badly at the moment, it is good for the scientist to live in the constant presence of the great visions that science offers.

In what follows,[1] I lay particular stress on modern biology, its inherent value, and its influence on the general life of mankind. Biology, especially in its relations to physics and chemistry, is the science I know best. Moreover, I believe that biology is now at the very center of scientific activity, and that its recent and probable future discoveries have the profoundest human implications.

[1] Parts of this chapter are drawn from the Seymour Korkes Memorial Lecture, which I delivered at Duke University on April 6, 1967. I wish to thank my colleagues there, and in particular Dr. and Mrs. Philip Handler, for the hospitality shown to me during that visit.

Some Effects of Science in the Modification of Ethical Values

What I have said hitherto applies largely to science as seen by the scientist himself, but the relation of science to human values extends far beyond this. The great vistas of space and time which modern science has opened up, the perspectives of evolution, and the interrelation of all living creatures—these affect the outlook of vast numbers of people throughout the world today. I am tempted to say "of most people," but this would be untrue, since hundreds of millions of people in the world today live completely without knowledge of these conceptions that modern science has introduced. Nevertheless such knowledge, rapidly or slowly, spreads and permeates the thought of people everywhere and modifies their outlook and their aspirations.

Some scientists and philosophers have said that science is ethically neutral, without influence on human values—that it is significant only as a tool, enabling us to realize our aims more effectively but in itself without influence on the nature of those aims. This I do not believe. In doing experiments and recording results, of course, it is essential to guard against our own desires and preconceptions, and to do everything we can to avoid letting them distort our findings. But in the larger sense, as science grows, as our broad picture of the world and of man is enlarged and deepened by it, and as its consequences for the world become ever more apparent, it becomes one of the major forces that modifies and remolds our concepts of what is good, what is tolerable, and what is intolerable in human life and conduct. These are not abstract issues; they involve many of the deepest personal and social conflicts of our time.

The relation between the progress of science and the change in our sense of values is obvious in many things. A polluted city water supply was at one time an unpleasant but tolerated nuisance; when it became known that it was also a carrier of typhoid fever and other diseases it became in effect a crime to tolerate such things. After these achievements of modern public health, which came toward the beginning of our century, or even earlier, we are again threatened by pollution on a far wider scale than before—a pollution that threatens the whole environment. To this grave problem I return later.

In matters of still deeper human import, also, such as the institution of slavery, the progress of science and technology has led gradually to a profound change in moral attitudes. For centuries a few sensitive and high-minded men denounced the practice of human slavery, but it persisted because it was woven deeply into the economic structure of most earlier societies. As technical advances made new sources of energy available, the compelling need for slave labor grew less and approached the vanishing point; in Europe and America hardheaded businessmen joined the humanitarian idealists, and practical politicians rallied to support the antislavery movement. I do not mean, of course, that the progress of science was the only reason for the abolition of slavery—the world is far too complex to be explained by any such simple theories—but the scientific advances were an indispensable component of the whole change in moral outlook.

One of the most profound changes in general outlook in our time—a change common to East and West, though manifested in different ways—is the rising general conviction that a good life is possible for most men on this earth. Men are discarding the past attitude of resignation to a world predominantly characterized by suffering and want, in which they looked to a better world to come, having few hopes of this one. Now increasingly their desires and hopes are centered in the present world. One may approve or disapprove this trend; that, for the moment, is not the point. These new hopes may prove to be illusory, in view of the grim realities of the world today. My point is that the trend exists, that it represents a fundamental shift in the value judgments of mankind, and that it is a direct consequence of the progress of pure and applied science.

The very temper and attitude of mind that permit science to flourish must in themselves produce conflicts with many traditional values. The scientist is forced to guard against his preconceptions, to be on the watch for them and eliminate them whenever possible, to regard all his conclusions as in some degree tentative and subject to further modification in the light of experience. This attitude may remain limited; the scientist may apply it only to the particular range of problems that he deals with in the laboratory; but inevitably it tends to spread and becomes the basis of our approach to broader issues. Inevitably it is disturbing, for it clashes with traditional ways of thought and dogmatic belief, which are deeply rooted; these are the product of generations of men, and they are charged with powerful emotions. These traditional attitudes are generally the product of instinctive wisdom; they have grown up without logical foundation, as useful beliefs generally do, but with profound relevance to human needs in the society in which they arose. As the world changes, these beliefs may become irrelevant, sometimes dangerously irrelevant; and in our time such changes are brought about predominantly by the progress of science and technology. The scientist generally sees these changes and their implications sooner than most other people; this is not surprising, since, generally, scientists have helped to bring them about.

I see three great areas today in which the clash between the traditional wisdom and the forces that compel a revision of our outlook is particularly acute—first, in our attitude to war, aggression and resistance to aggression; second, in human fertility and the command to be fruitful and multiply; and third, in the need to guard and improve our natural resources rather than squandering them. All three are intimately related. The most precious of all our natural resources is the biological and social inheritance of mankind, and this is threatened by modern war, in a manner totally unprecedented. One of the major pressures that can lead to war, now as in the past, is the pressure of expanding and hungry populations; and this has increased, and is increasing, with a speed hitherto unknown. Population growth is likewise the great devourer of natural resources. Science and technology have shown that it is possible to make the world a pleasanter place for the ordinary man than he could ever have dreamed in the past. When there are more people than ever before, and each man asks more of the good things of life than ever before in history, we consume more food, more metals, more fuels, in fifty years than in all the previous history of mankind; and even this is small compared to what we may expect in the next fifty years.[2]

I return later to these themes, after turning first to some of the major advances in modern biology and their implications.

The Revolution in Biochemistry and Molecular Biology: Achievements and Prospects

In 1923 J. B. S. Haldane, one of the most versatile scientists of our time, published a small booklet called "Daedalus: or Science and the Future." In this he predicted that, although the center of scientific interest at that time lay in physics, our century in science would be preeminently the era of biology. Haldane began his scientific career as a biochemist; he became an eminent geneticist; and it is significant that

---

[2] I have spoken here necessarily in broad general terms; the detailed evidence is to be found in many places. See for instance that fascinating and disturbing book by Harrison Brown, *The Challenge of Man's Future* (New York: The Viking Press, 1954).

the most dramatic advances in modern biology have come in the fusion of these two fields of research. However, Haldane's prophecy appeared to remain unfulfilled for some twenty years after he made it. In spite of many brilliant advances in biology and biochemistry, the period from 1920 to 1945 was predominantly the period of great advances in nuclear physics. Since the end of World War II, however, events have abundantly verified Haldane's prophecy. A great turning point in biology came, indeed, in a paper published in the midst of the war. Avery, MacLeod, and McCarty in 1944 demonstrated that the "transforming factor" of pneumococcus, which brought about the transformation of this organism from a form without a capsule to an encapsulated form, was deoxyribonucleic acid (DNA); thus DNA was indeed the essential material for transmitting hereditary information. For some years the full significance of this epoch-making discovery was unappreciated; indeed it was not until 1953, when Crick and Watson deduced the two-chain structure of DNA, coiled in a double helix, that a clear-cut chemical basis for understanding the transmission of hereditary information emerged.

These achievements launched the prodigious development of what is now commonly called molecular biology. However, we must remember that the recent rapid advances were made possible by a long previous period of solid but less spectacular developments, in genetics and in biochemistry, extending over a period of a century or more. The patient laborious investigations of the chemists who investigated proteins from about 1840 on, and nucleic acids from 1870 on, laid the essential foundations of structural knowledge that were necessary for the rapid flowering of molecular biology in the last twenty years. Classical genetics, beginning with Mendel, and continuing with William Bateson, T. H. Morgan, H. J. Muller, and many others, had built up a magnificent and largely self-contained theory of genes and their manifestations in organisms, solidly based on a vast number of experimental facts.[3] Shortly after 1900, proof was obtained that the genes were located in the chromosomes, within the cell nucleus; but their chemical nature remained obscure until the work of Avery *et al* and of Crick and Watson.[4] Each of the two complementary strands of the DNA helix is a chain with many links, perhaps tens or hundreds of thousands; but there are only four different kinds of links. These are the four purine and pyrimidine bases, which for short we may designate as A, G, C, and T. Of these, G in one chain is complementary to C in the other, and conversely; similarly for A and T. Thus a short section of the double helix might be represented diagrammatically by a pattern such as:

-G-T-T-C-A-A-A-C-G-

. . . .

. . . .

. . . .

-C-A-A-G-T-T-T-G-C-

Here the upper and lower lines of letters represent short segments of the two complementary chains of the helix. The vertical dotted lines connecting the upper and lower lines are symbols for the hydrogen bonds which chemically determine the complementary relations. Note that G in one chain is always opposite C in the other, and A is opposite T; thus the sequence in either chain completely specifies that in the other. Each chain has thus a pattern complementary to the other; on replication, each guides the formation of a chain complementary to itself, and thus both are reproduced. In proteins there is nothing like this sort of complementarity,

---

[3] See T. H. Morgan, *The Theory of the Gene* (New Haven: Yale University Press, 1925).

[4] For a further historical account of the development of ideas concerning the nature of the genetic material, see for instance B. Glass, "A Century of Biochemical Genetics," *Proceedings of the American Philosophical Society*, 109 (1965), 227.

thus proteins are not suitable as the transmitters of hereditary information. It is the pattern of the sequence in the four bases in each chain that contains the information transmitted to the next generation, by replication of the DNA. By another process, known as transcription, the DNA chains of the cell nucleus form complementary chains of ribonucleic acid (RNA) containing the four bases G, C, A, and U (the latter in RNA corresponds to T in DNA, and is closely related to it). These pass from the nucleus into the cytoplasm, attach themselves there to the structures known as ribosomes, and thereby serve to guide the formation of proteins.

Proteins are synthesized, like nucleic acids, in the form of long chains with many links. In this case these links are the twenty amino acid residues that are found everywhere in nature, from bacteria to man. It is now clear that a triplet of successive bases in the nucleic acids determines a single amino acid residue in a protein chain: for instance, the triplet sequence UAU or UAC determines the amino acid tyrosine and AAA or AAG determines lysine. The mutation of a single unit in one of these triplets can lead to the appearance of a different amino acid residue in the protein whose structure is determined by the gene in question. Such changes indeed are the fundamental units of biological mutation.

This set of relations between the base triplets and the amino acids constitutes the genetic code, which specifies the relation between the nucleic acids and the proteins whose structures they specify.[5] The proteins, in turn, play the central

[5] The best general survey of modern molecular biology is probably J. D. Watson's *Molecular Biology of the Gene* (New York: W. A. Benjamin, 1965). It is written with great lucidity but requires a basic knowledge of chemistry. On a more technical level the symposium on *The Genetic Code* (Cold Spring Harbor, N.Y.: Cold Spring Harbor Symposia in Quantitative Biology, 1966), Vol. XXXI, presents an impressive array of recent discoveries. One may particularly recommend the opening article by F. H. C. Crick, "The Genetic Code—Yesterday, Today, and Tomorrow."

part in almost all the other activities of the organism. They constitute the structural framework of tissues like muscle, tendon, and hair; and in their myriad different forms they become enzymes that catalyze every biochemical process.

Proteins are molecules of such complexity that for a long time it seemed an almost hopeless task to decipher their structure in detail. During the last twenty years, however, the structures of a substantial number of proteins have been completely worked out. Not only do we know the exact order of the amino acid residues in many proteins, but in several instances—as with the oxygen-carrying protein myoglobin and the enzyme lysozyme, which attacks bacterial cell walls —we know with high precision the three-dimensional architecture of the molecule and the arrangement of the active site where the enzyme attacks its substrate. Moreover, the synthesis of proteins by the organic chemists, which seemed an impossible dream a few years ago, is now becoming a reality. Insulin, one of the simpler proteins, has now been made synthetically by three groups of researchers, one of them in China. There is every prospect that, within a generation, chemists will create synthetic enzymes to catalyze reactions not promoted by any enzyme found in nature. Thereby they may produce in industrial chemistry a revolution that will permit many processes, now proceeding only at high temperature and in poor yield, to run smoothly and with high yield at ordinary temperatures.

Regulation of Biochemical Activity

In recent years we have gained new insight into the factors that regulate and control the operations of living organisms. That organisms require such regulatory mechanisms has been apparent since the time of Aristotle, and probably since long before. In modern times such concepts were emphasized in the nineteenth century by Claude Bernard, who pointed out that the constancy of the internal environment—*i.e.*, primarily the circulating blood, in higher organisms—is an essential condition for the freedom of the organism. Walter Cannon expanded the concept of homeostasis, including the regulatory controls involved in the interaction of the hormones and the organs on which they act; and the integrative action of the nervous system had been manifest long before Sir Charles Sherrington published a famous book with that title just over sixty years ago.

In recent years, biochemists have discovered the existence of regulatory controls at a deeper level. Not only does the genetic material contain the regions that direct the synthesis of specific proteins; these regions are under the control of other genetic factors, the operator genes, that determine whether the biosynthesis of specific proteins under the control of a given operator, shall or shall not proceed. The synthetic processes cannot be allowed to run at full speed all the time; that would be intolerably wasteful. The proteins manufactured under the guidance of the genetic material are not wanted all the time or in unlimited quantities. Much of the time—indeed most of the time, for many genes—the operator gene is held in check by the attachment of a repressor; this "turns off" the synthesis of the specific enzymes that are under the control of a particular operator. If the cell lacks the molecules on which these enzymes act, there is no need to produce the enzymes. If such molecules then enter the cell, they may act as "inducers," combining with the repressor and thereby causing it to release its grip on the operator gene, so that the synthesis of the necessary enzymes can proceed. Thus, in the economy of the cell, these enzymes are manufactured only when needed.[6] There is now decisive evidence, due primarily to very recent work of Walter Gilbert and Mark Ptashne at Harvard, that the repressor molecules are proteins. Although these genetic mechanisms have been established most clearly in bacteria, it seems almost certain that similar processes operate in all higher organisms also.

Another form of control, feedback inhibition, operates, not to prevent formation of the enzyme, but to regulate its activity after it is formed. Many biochemical processes involve sequences of reactions which lead to the synthesis of some essential chemical substance, from the starting materials that the cell has available. Starting with a substance A, for example, the sequence may lead to an essential biochemical substance F by a series of intermediate steps, each catalyzed by a specific enzyme:

$$A \rightarrow B \rightarrow C \rightarrow D \rightarrow E \rightarrow F$$

If substance F accumulates, beyond the current needs of the organism, it is obviously economical to shut down the whole process, partially or completely. In feedback inhibition this is indeed what occurs: F combines with the enzyme that converts A to B, and the F-enzyme combination thereby loses its capacity to catalyze this process. If B is not being made, all the later steps in the process automatically shut down also, since the starting material is no longer available. If the concentration of F falls, the F-enzyme complex dissociates, the free enzyme becomes active once more, and the whole process resumes. Such processes beautifully regulate the flow of matter and energy in the cell; they serve to insure that there is enough but not too much of each of the various essential metabolic substances. It is a beautiful piece of biological engineering, which makes exacting demands on the design of the enzyme that catalyzes the conversion of A to B. This enzyme not only binds molecule A, in the process of converting it to B; it must also bind F, a very different molecule, at some other point of attachment on the enzyme surface; and the binding of F must somehow alter the enzyme reversibly so that its capacity to convert A to B is temporarily diminished or abolished. In spite of these stringent specifications, enzymes that fulfill them have evolved again and again, and they are of the utmost importance in biology.[6]

These advances in our understanding of biological regulation foreshadow future advances in areas still uncharted. Perhaps the domain of our greatest ignorance in biology today is in the field of development. How does a complex organism, with its many different organs and with complicated interactions between them, emerge from a fertilized ovum? The anatomical patterns in the development of the embryo have been known in detail for a long time; but the underlying nature of the processes involved, on the molecular level, is still most obscure. The great advances of recent years in biochemical genetics, and in the processes of regulatory control—so briefly sketched above—offer suggestive clues that may lead to a future revolution in our understanding of development and differentiation. No one can forecast the time and character of a scientific revolution before it occurs, but there is a pervading belief among biologists that such a revolution in our knowledge of development is sure to come, and that it is not very far away. When it comes, it will certainly throw floods of light on matters and problems now obscure—on the nature and control of cancer, for example, and on other problems that may be of still greater importance to mankind.

Some Effects and Implications of Modern Biology

What now of the direct effects, on mankind at large, of the revolutionary new knowledge in biochemistry and genetics? As yet the intellectual excitement this new knowledge has generated has far outrun its practical effects; but such effects

[6] Much of our insight into these phenomena is due to J. Monod, F. Jacob, and their collaborators. For further information, see, for instance, J. Monod, J.-P. Changeux, and F. Jacob, "Allosteric Proteins and Cellular Control Systems," *Journal of Molecular Biology*, 6 (1963), 306; D. E. Atkinson, "Regulation of Enzyme Activity," *Annual Review of Biochemistry*, 35 (1966), 85; J. T. Edsall, "The Organization of Protein Molecules for Regulatory Processes in Biology," *Proceedings of the American Philosophical Society*, 111 (1967), 59.

are sure to follow, as they have from other great fundamental discoveries.

One practical effect is to emphasize a major aspect of the conservation movement—the conservation of the most precious of our natural resources, our genetic heritage. The integrity of the thin delicate threads of the nucleic acids, with their encoded patterns of base sequences, is essential to the future of mankind, as to all other living creatures. Consciousness of this responsibility has led to greatly increased care in the medical use of X rays. It has also influenced public policy, for public awareness of the genetic dangers of radiation was certainly one of the factors that led to the limited nuclear test ban treaty of 1963. (Personally I would rate the slowing of the nuclear arms race as a far more important reason for the treaty, but that does not affect the point made above.) And it has implanted widely the conviction that a nuclear war, for whatever cause it might be fought, would be an unprecedented crime against mankind—in the most literal sense, a betrayal of our inheritance, on a colossal scale. Apart from the hundreds of millions of deaths, the vast social disruption, the desolation of the land, and the ecological changes that such a war would bring, there is the consciousness that the descendants of the survivors would pay a terrible price—exacted by us—for countless generations to come. Insofar as knowledge of genetics is widely diffused and deeply understood throughout the nations of the world, it can act as one influence toward sanity and restraint in the effort to prevent nuclear war.

What of the hopes for more positive aid to mankind from genetic knowledge? I am as yet mistrustful of programs for positive eugenics; I believe that we still know far too little about human heredity to offer wise and practicable plans for improving the quality of the human race. Social policies that encourage the intelligent and able to have children, and discourage the incompetent and shiftless from having them, should do some genetic good and are unlikely to do harm;

but in view of our present ignorance, one should not exaggerate the possible good. Nor should we concentrate too heavily on intelligence as a quality to be promoted by genetic selection; kindheartedness and generosity of spirit are at least as important for a good world, and the best parents do not always have the best brains.

The great recent advances in genetics have come chiefly from the study of bacteria and viruses. However, there is, I think, some reason to hope that our knowledge of human heredity may increase profoundly in the next generation. It is now readily possible to examine the chromosomes of man or any other species, quite rapidly and simply, and to detect abnormalities that before could have been overlooked. Moreover, with modern tissue-culture techniques, we can propagate cells from human tissues and study them in culture. In such cultures it may be possible to make a far more detailed genetic analysis of the constitution of a particular individual than is possible today, and perhaps to detect recessive genes, not apparent in the phenotype of the individual himself, that would otherwise remain unknown until they might appear in homozygous form in some of his descendants. One may even imagine a file of such genetic data for each individual, and a computer program in which prospective mates could combine their personal data and receive in reply an evaluation of at least some of the characteristics of their possible children. Clearly this is at present a flight of fantasy, but I believe that it is nevertheless a genuine possibility.

Some eminent biologists, notably Joshua Lederberg, have proposed programs of "genetic engineering" whereby undesirable genes could be modified in, or lacking genes introduced into, people suffering from genetic abnormalities.[7] In bacteria this can be done by transformation, as in the studies

[7] See, for instance, J. Lederberg "Biological Future of Man" in *Man and his Future*, A Ciba Foundation Symposium (London: J. & A. Churchill, 1963), p. 270; also E. L. Tatum "The Possibility of Manipulating Genetic Change" in *Genetics and the Future of Man*, J. D. Roslansky, ed. (New York: Appleton-Century-Crofts, 1966),

of Avery, MacLeod, and McCarty, but also by transduction, in which new genetic material is introduced into the bacterium by way of a bacterial virus. One cannot copy these techniques in any simple way when dealing with man or any higher organism. Nevertheless, with the aid of tissue-culture techniques, and their genetic manipulation, it may be possible to introduce modifications, or replace missing genes, by some form of transfer, in human cell cultures and reimplant the modified cells in the person who needs them. The actual achievement of any such treatment is still not a practical prospect; no one yet knows how it may be done. However, the possibility of doing it is very real indeed. How such things may be done wisely, and without harmful side effects, if indeed we do learn to do them at all, is a matter for earnest and careful thought. The possible may become the actual sooner than we think.

Multiplication of Mankind and Deterioration of the Human Environment

The recent advances in molecular biology and the genetic code represent a great triumph of basic science, with many implications for the future of man. However, the applications of biology with the most far-reaching effects on man in our time arise from earlier advances in fundamental science. Public health measures and applied microbiology have reduced infectious disease from the major preoccupation of physicians to a relatively minor role; the general run of problems that a doctor encounters in his practice is now quite different from what it was in 1900. I would not join those optimists who claim that infectious disease will soon be a thing of the past. Man will continue to live in a world full

---

p. 51. Several of the other articles in this volume are also of great interest in the present connection; I would mention particularly those by Bentley Glass, Paul Ramsey, and Kingsley Davis.

of bacteria and viruses, most of which are harmless to him or indeed beneficent. Some, however, will continue to cause disease and to develop resistance to antibiotics; we may achieve a biological balance between man and the microorganisms at a much lower level of infection than in the past, but I do not expect infectious disease to disappear.[8] However, the decline in infectious disease, partly from the use of antibiotics and pesticides, but largely from fundamentally simple public health measures like the purification of water and pasteurization of milk, has shifted the whole center of gravity of the world's major problems. Mankind, instead of struggling to maintain its numbers in the face of disease and early death, is now overwhelmed by population increase, with the prospect of doubling the world's present population within twenty-five to thirty years. Over most of the world, in Asia, Latin America, and Africa, where the rates of increase are the greatest, population increase is running ahead of food supply. A recent study[9] shows that, throughout Central and South America, population growth runs well ahead of the growth in gross national product per capita. These facts mean that sheer hunger is one of the most terrible medical and human problems of today. Hunger not only kills; it can stunt and cripple its victims for life. The most widespread form of malnutrition, the protein deficiency kwashiorkor, afflicts countless millions of children throughout the world. If they survive, they are likely to have suffered permanent damage, both in body and mind. It is a grim fact that we live in a world where more people than ever before are prosperous and well fed; yet it is also a world where more people than

[8] For a detailed and searching discussion of the points briefly mentioned here, see René Dubos, *Man Adapting* (New Haven: Yale University Press, 1966).

[9] See *Population Bulletin XXIII*, No. 3, June, 1967 (Washington, D.C. [1755 Massachusetts Ave., N. W.], Population Reference Bureau, Inc.) Earlier issues of this bulletin contain much valuable information on population problems.

ever before are in hunger and misery. Both statements can be true, because there are more people.

Even apart from the problem of hunger, population growth threatens the livable qualities of the world. Living space disappears, noise increases, forests are cut down, rivers, lakes, and air become more polluted. As these trends progress, most people are losing what was once the birthright even of the poor—space, some sense of quiet, clean air, and water.

It is tragic that an era of supremely great discoveries in biology should also be an era of unparalleled destruction of animal life. All over the world, as human population multiplies and industrialization proceeds, species after species of animals and birds have become extinct or are threatened with extinction. With modern mechanized equipment, whales can be killed at rates incomparably greater than ever before. The modern whaling industry appears to be hunting the whales to extinction and thereby of course destroying itself. Whether human restraint and foresight can avert this tragic end remains to be seen. In the desert country of Arabia and North Africa, hunters with modern motorized equipment can hunt down game animals with ease, and many of these are apparently on the way to extinction also. The widespread use of chemical pesticides has almost certainly wrought immense destruction of birds and fishes, and perhaps of some animals also.[10] And of course the spread of human population has devoured much of the habitat of many animal species. The rich variety of living creatures that our ancestors knew may be a thing of the past, just as many of our rich and varied landscapes are being reduced to dull uniformity by the highway and the bulldozer. Our descendants may be compelled to live in a world that has lost irretrievably much of its color and variety, although they will perhaps have the consolation of not knowing what they are missing.

Modern science has endowed us with immense powers.

[10] See for instance the pesticide report of the President's Science Advisory Committee, 1963; summarized in *Science*, 140 (1963), 878.

We can alter the world, on a vast scale, more rapidly than ever before; and we can do so without realizing the ramifications of the forces we have set in motion. The use of chemical pesticides is a striking example: they killed noxious insects, improved crop yields dramatically, and nearly wiped out malaria and some other diseases in certain areas. It took time to discover their widespread toxic action and the damage they did to the ecology of many regions, and then to begin restricting their use within well-defined limits, eliminating altogether some of the most dangerous and developing new and specific pesticides directed against particular classes of insects and not toxic to organisms in general.[11]

If we are to avoid future disasters that could arise from misuse of our great powers to change environment, it is imperative to think of the world as a complex interrelated system in which a modification introduced anywhere produces, not only the effect immediately intended, but other effects that flow from the interactions within the system. The physicians and public health officers who did so much to wipe out infectious disease did not foresee the terrible problems of population growth that would follow. The trained experts who introduced DDT and other pesticides knew what they wanted to achieve, and for the moment at least, they largely achieved it; but surely they failed to foresee the gravity of the complications that followed. As troubles arise, corrective steps are taken, sooner or later, and the damage begins to be corrected. In future, however, we cannot afford to wait for the damage to be done; the situation cries out for more foresight, for a searching and detailed analysis of the whole interacting system into which we propose to introduce some new modification.[12] Analogous to the type of analysis

11 See C. M. Williams, "The Third Generation Pesticides," *Scientific American*, July, 1967.
12 A relatively simple but still somewhat complex system that illustrates such interactions is the blood in its interactions with oxygen and carbon dioxide. See L. J. Henderson, *Blood* (New Haven: Yale University Press, 1928).

developed at such places as the RAND Corporation, to deal with problems of military strategy, might well be employed on a larger scale to deal with the great problems of the interaction of organisms, including man, with their environment. Foresight, of course, will never be perfect; in our analysis of problems we must work with simplified models of the actual world. Even after the most careful analysis some of the results of introducing any major change into the world will be unexpected. But with constant vigilance we can incorporate the causes of the unexpected findings into our model, correct initial forecasts, and adjust policy accordingly. With power must go restraint: we can change the world so fast, and often so dangerously, that we shall increasingly be compelled to think deeply before taking new major actions if we are to survive.

In his book *The Next Million Years* Sir Charles Galton Darwin suggested that our descendants might look back upon the present era as the Golden Age of human prosperity. He portrayed a future in which the pressure of population on resources would continue unremittingly in devastating fashion, with profound unrest and the constant threat of war. For us who are here now it is hard to think of the present time, with all its fears and horrors, as a Golden Age. Nevertheless, for people like myself, who live in a wealthy and fortunate country and have taken part in the great adventure of modern science, it has been an inspiring time to live in. It remains to be seen whether we can disprove the validity of Darwin's somber forecast for the generations to come. Even if we are wise enough to avert the catastrophe of nuclear war, the rich countries may slowly drown in the pollution produced by the consequences of their own affluence, and rich and poor alike might eventually be overwhelmed by failure to solve the great problems of food, space, and natural resources.

Modern biology has achieved deep new insight into the

nature of all living creatures, from bacteria to man, with prospects of still more important discoveries following in the next generation. The wise use of applied science and technology for the benefit of man, however, is a problem whose full dimensions we have scarcely begun to envisage; and few as yet appreciate its urgency. It involves not only the scientists but also the politicians and all other people of the world and we must face it adequately if we are to have hope for the future of man.

11

FROM SOCIAL ENGINEERING TO CREATIVE CHARITY

JOHN T. NOONAN, JR.

University of California, Berkeley

I T IS THE DISCOVERY of every first-year student of law that there is no law written down anywhere which he can look up and apply to solve the problem before him. The hundreds of books of statutes, the thousands of case reports, the multitudinous volumes of learned legal treatises which line the shelves of the law library may be relevant to the problem; they do not answer it. The answer, the response of a living human being to a fresh human question, is given only by a human being himself, analyzing the present facts, testing, selecting, and combining the answers to past problems, and reacting in the light of this new synthesis to the situation before him. It is thus that the student, discarding the preconceptions of the layman, learns that law for him is not the words of statutes to be memorized or the precedents established by predecessors to be revered but a process in which he is to be a vital and creative participant.

Prophets of the future may foresee mechanization as the most measurable change that technological development can bring to law. But the view of law as process is so firmly engrained in student and practitioner that mechanization of the technological kind predicted holds no special significance for them. It will be possible to feed statutes, cases, treatises, into a great computer that will then do the work of identifying and compiling "governing law" and analogies.[1] Such a computer when perfected will mean a considerable reduction in the work of junior lawyers. Its effective use, however, will depend on analysis of the case before computerization occurs, and what the computer provides will be only the raw ingredients of law. The lawyer's essential task of deciding the law of the situation before him will remain. Enabled to collect past relevant data more swiftly, the lawyer as a person trained in the process will still have to respond to the matter at hand.

Law is a process, and it is because this is so that I would view as foolish any attempt to foretell the substantive rules that may govern American business, family life, or use of the automobile or narcotion fifty years from now. Stability of rule is not characteristic of the common law.[2] Great change in legal rule occurred in the course of nineteenth-century industrialization in an underpopulated and relatively isolated United States. It would not seem that a denser population and closer relations with other countries would lessen the rate of change. How particular statutes and precedents may survive could only be a guess. The rules may be expected to change in response to technological innovation, to population rates,

[1] See William B. Eldridge and Sally F. Dennis, "The Computer as a Tool for Legal Research," *Law and Contemporary Problems*, 28 (1963), 78–99. A commercial company based in New York, Law Research Service, Inc., already provides computer research to law firms and law libraries throughout the country. Citations are given by teletype immediately, excerpts from opinions are given within a day; the charge is twelve dollars per query.

[2] Dean Pound wrote in 1936, "Even in a reasonably modified form it is not easy to maintain a doctrine of identity or continuity of rules of law for the common-law world. . . . As we look back over our legal history, we cannot but be struck with the relatively short life of rules of law, *i.e.*, of legal precepts affixing definite detailed consequences to definite detailed states of fact." Roscoe Pound, "What is the Common-Law?" in *The Future of the Common Law* (Cambridge: Harvard Tercentenary Publications, 1936).

to shifts in theological and moral beliefs, to all the other factors affecting the physical and social environment. For example, the rules on negligence have been elaborated largely in response to the introduction of machinery into daily life. The technological development asked for a legal response. As the most familiar of mechanisms, the automobile, continues to be put to lethal use, it is not improbable that at some future point, absolute liability for injury resulting therefrom will be imputed to the manufacturers on the theory that they make an instrument that is inherently dangerous.[3] Such a result will be more likely if the automobile death rate mounts with an ever increased use of cars and it becomes evident that much safer cars are technologically feasible. For another example, the rules governing the origin of life will have to respond to the possibilities of banks of stored spermatozoa, of the transplantation of ova, of the existence of embryos outside the uterus. It may be guessed that legal protection for the rights of the child produced by artificial insemination will be extended.[4] It may be guessed that the rights of the embryo in any form will receive even greater legal recognition[5] and that this development of tort law will counteract the strong pressures to extend the legalization of abortion. But all these surmises are speculation. The wisdom of the common law is not to decide cases before they arise; only when cases are argued are the major consequences of decision graspable. It is to follow this wisdom not to predict what specific rules will be adopted. All that may be expected is substantial change.

[3] In short, what may be expected is an application to automobile manufacturers of the classic torts doctrine of *Ryland v. Fletcher*, 1868, *Law Reports*, 3 House of Lords 330. See, in general, on the impetus to impose strict liability, Harry H. Ognall, "Some Facets of Strict Tortious Liability in the United States and Their Implications," *Notre Dame Lawyer*, 33 (1958), 239, 272.

[4] See Note, "Social and Legal Aspects of Human Artificial Insemination," *Wisconsin Law Review*, 858 (1965), 884.

[5] David A. Gordon, "The Unborn Plaintiff," *Michigan Law Review*, 63 (1965), 579, 627.

Plunged into the flow, the lawyers will respond to the changing environment with a thousand shifts, expedients, improvisations, and these in turn will become the statutes and precedents of a more remote day. What will be law will be the process of response.

Yet law is not only a process in the sense I have suggested of trained persons responding to their environment. It is a process in which the lawyer interacts with other human persons. The observation may appear obvious, but it seems necessary in view of the emphasis often placed by lawyers on the process without reference to persons. The most influential example of a process-oriented approach is the *Report on Professional Responsibility*, prepared in 1958 by a joint conference of the Association of American Law Schools and the American Bar Association. This states, "The lawyer's highest loyalty is at the same time the most intangible. It is a loyalty that runs, not to persons, but to procedures and institutions."[6] In context, this statement may be read as only a laudable rejection of the view that loyalty to a client is the measure of a lawyer's duty. The superior loyalty the report proposes, however, seems not only intangible, like all virtues, but abstract, lacking in concrete substance, and purposeless. Why should a lawyer be loyal to process? Is the spinning of the wheels of a court more sacred than the spinning of the wheels of a mill? Process here seems to be proposed as an end in itself, removed from the life of the lawyer and the lives of other persons his acts affect. Such a view of the law is too unreal to provide a basis for prediction of law's development. Process invokes loyalty because it serves persons, and persons are the realities by which the lawyer's conduct is measured. The law is process by which a lawyer acts and affects himself and other human beings.

What may be said of the future of law must be said of this process related to persons. Here one ventures on no easy

---

6 "Professional Responsibility: Report of the Joint Conference," *American Bar Association Journal*, 44 (1958), 1161.

guesses about the future of a rule but on a sounding of broad philosophical tendencies as these tendencies are reflected and, in turn, shaped, in the special world of lawyers. The course of American legal history has been to pass from an emphasis on law as the assertion of individual rights in the nineteenth century to an emphasis on law as social engineering in the twentieth century.[7] The lawyers' view of their function has made this change possible. What will the lawyers' future concept of their function be?

I would answer this question with a paradox: individualism will decline, personalism will increase. The paradox is resolved by identifying individualism in this context as the doctrine that any single individual who has the economic ability may hire a lawyer and may expect him to carry out orders so far as law permits; while personalism in this context is the belief that each person has a right to the aid of a lawyer in case of need, a right that is qualified by the requirement that respect must be accorded the conscience of the lawyer. I shall give two examples of declining individualism. First, consider the evolution of the concept of the trial. A trial, according to the individualists, is designed for the satisfaction of the parties. Its purpose is not to discover truth but to satisfy the participants' combativeness. It is a substitute for physical combat.[8] In the course of it, violence and such peaceful means as bribery, forgery, and some forms of perjury are excluded; yet nondisclosure of evidence, half-truths, and perjurious self-serving by one's client are permitted. Open appeal to the emotions of the jury is acceptable. Cross-examination to discredit a truthful witness is desirable. A lawyer must fight for his client with the utmost zeal.[9]

---

[7] Roscoe Pound, "Fifty Years of Jurisprudence," *Harvard Law Review*, 50 (1937), 557 and 51 (1938), 810–12.

[8] The most perceptive presentation of this view is Charles Curtis, *It's Your Law* (1954), pp. 17–21

[9] See Monroe H. Freedman, "Professional Responsibility of the Criminal Defense Lawyer: The Three Hardest Questions," *Michigan Law Review*, 64 (1966), 1469–84.

This concept of a trial still has its defenders, and it corresponds to the practice of many advocates today. However, the concept is in transition. It has been rejected by the important statement of the American law schools and the American Bar Association referred to above. The new concept of the trial is that it is designed for the discovery of truth, and the adversary system is justified only as it serves this end. In this view, the adversary system is defended because it prevents a tribunal from coming too quickly to a conclusion, from too readily stamping a particular view on facts, because it preserves a heuristic tension in the minds of the triers of the case. It provides a "social framework within which one's capacity for impartial judgment can attain its fullest realization."[10] The adversary system itself is not likely to disappear. But this rationale of the system will exclude all the lying means, the irrelevant attacks on the opponents, and most of the rhetoric that has been dear to the defenders of the individual's right to a fight.

There are clear signs that the view of the trial as rational investigation is gaining ground. One such indication is the shift in what is considered good technique in arguing a case to a court. There will always be some element of emotional appeal in advocacy, for men are not pure intellects, and emotion may properly be employed to aid the response to truth. But the harangues of the past, the efforts of a Charles Choate or a Clarence Darrow, seem curiously old-fashioned,[11] and they seem old-fashioned because of their resort to emotional irrelevancies. It would seem likely that the advocate of the future would place even less reliance on the art of the orator.

Beyond the changing style of argumentation, another sign is the use of the procedures known as discovery and pretrial.

---

[10] *Op. cit. supra*, note 6, p. 1161.

[11] For an example of Darrow, see Arthur Weinberg, *Attorney for the Damned*, p. 139 (1957); for an example of Choate, see Robert Swaine, *The Cravath Firm*, 2, 60–62.

By discovery, information known to the adversary is forced to disclosure before trial. In pretrial a hearing is held before the trial; it is the apex of discovery; an experienced judge describes it as "an indispensable tool in assuring a fair trial."[12] The federal courts have here set a standard that will be followed eventually by laggard localities. By these devices of reason, trials are already being rationalized.

A third index of change is the increasingly strict standards of rationality imposed on the government in criminal prosecutions. The prosecutor is now compelled to respond to the broad discovery rights of the accused, is prohibited from suppressing evidence helpful to the accused, is required to make available to the accused the names of material witnesses, and must call the accused's attention to the doubtful credibility of the prosecutor's own witness.[13] A trial "no longer can be properly considered a game of wits and skill."[14] It might be argued that these restrictions on the prosecution can be regarded only as restrictions on the disproportionate power of the government, not as milestones toward rationality. But on July 1, 1966, the Supreme Court put into effect a rule conditioning the accused's right of discovery upon the defendant's giving the government a limited right of discovery.[15] This was the first step to establishment of a

---

[12] Irving R. Kaufman, "The Philosophy of Effective Judicial Supervision over Litigation," in "Proceedings of the Seminar on Procedures for Effective Judicial Administration," *Federal Rules Decisions*, 29 (1961), 214.

[13] The cases establishing these four propositions are, respectively, *Campbell v. United States*, 373 United States Reports (1963), 487; *Brady v. Maryland*, 373 United States Reports (1963), 83, 87; *United States ex. rel Meers v. Wilkins*, 326 Federal Reporter 2d 135 (2d Circuit 1964); *Curran v. Delaware*, 259 Federal Reporter 2d 707 (3d Circuit 1958), *certiorari denied* 358 United States Reports (1959), 948.

[14] *Curran v. Delaware, op. cit. supra*, p. 711.

[15] *Federal Rules of Criminal Procedure*, 16c. For what could well serve as a rationale for the change see William J. Brennan, Jr., "The Criminal Prosecution: Sporting Event or Quest for Truth," *Washington Law Quarterly* (1963), p. 293.

rule of candor for both prosecuting and defense attorneys. In the future it may be expected that standards will be imposed on the lawyers defending criminals as on the lawyers prosecuting them, and that eventually the same rules will be laid down for lawyers in civil litigation as those that now govern a federal prosecutor. The irrational is thus being gradually eliminated. In this process, what remains of nineteenth-century individualism's view of the lawyer as a fighter for his client will vanish.

My second example of the trend from individualism is the development of the group practice of law. Canon 35 of Professional Ethics of the American Bar Association, accepted in 1928, stated, "The professional services of a lawyer should not be controlled or exploited by any lay agency, personal or corporate, which intervenes between client and lawyer. A lawyer's relations to his client should be personal, and the responsibility should be directed to his client."[16] In the spirit of this canon the courts forbade the employment of lawyers by such groups as trade unions, real estate associations, and automobile clubs that desired to hire lawyers to serve their members.[17] A lawyer could have only an individual as a client; he could not be hired by a group to act for individuals in the group. In the 1960s, however, the principle of Canon 35 gave way before the twin pressures of the racial crisis and the desire to provide legal service to the poor. In 1962 the Supreme Court held that the National Association for the Advancement of Colored People could not constitutionally be prevented by a state from providing lawyers to parents who wanted to be plaintiffs in

[16] American Bar Association, *Canons of Professional Ethics*, Canon 35.
[17] E.g., *Chicago Bar Association v. Chicago Motor Club*, 362 Illinois Reports 50, 199 Northeastern Reporter 1st (1935); *In re Brotherhood of Railroad Trainmen*, 13 Illinois Reports 2d 391, 150 Northeastern Reporter 2d, 163 (1958); *Chicago Bar Association v. Friedlander*, 24 Illinois Reporter 2d 130, 164 Northeastern Reporter 2d, 517 (1960).

school desegregation cases. In 1964 the Court held that there was similar First and Fourteenth Amendment protection for a union that chose a particular lawyer and recommended him to its membership, thereby effectively channeling the legal business of the individual members to the approved lawyer.[18] In addition to civil rights organizations and trade unions, other groups such as teachers' associations, shipowners, and the Armed Forces now provide lawyers.[19] In California, where the fullest study of the need has been made, a committee of the Bar Association recommended in 1964 that a general rule be adopted permitting group legal services, provided that "the group has bona fide purposes other than providing legal services" and that there is "no group control over the lawyer in areas usually reserved for the attorney or the client."[20] Congress has permitted the Office of Economic Opportunity to support group legal practice, and it has provided federal backing for the establishment of neighborhood legal offices.[21] These offices are governed by nonprofit agencies and administered with "the maximum feasible participation of residents of the area and members of the groups." Cutting between lawyer and ultimate client, these local agencies determine basic policies and hire lawyers to serve the poor who qualify for help under the federal and local standards. Given constitutional protection and already exemplified in a variety of forms, group legal practice exists, and it may be expected to multiply enormously.

There has been and will be opposition. The Committee on

[18] The cases are respectively, *N.A.A.C.P. v. Button*, 371 United States Reports 415 (1962); *Brotherhood of Railroad Trainmen v. Virginia State Bar*, 377 United States Reports 1 (1964).

[19] Standing Committee of the California State Bar on Group Services, "Report on Group Legal Service," *California State Bar Journal*, 39 (1964), 652, 670–689.

[20] *Ibid*, 723.

[21] Economic Opportunity Act, Title 2, Section 202 (1964); *United States Code* 42, 2782.

the Unauthorized Practice of Law of the American Bar Association opposes the sweeping California proposal.[22] The reason is that group hiring of a lawyer works a revolution in the individualist's image of the lawyer's relations to his client. Between the lawyer and the individual he serves there now stands the group. Whatever area of tactical decision is left to the lawyer and the individual, it is likely that the policies of the group that pays him or recommends him will operate as a powerful influence upon his decisions. There is no longer a one-to-one lawyer-client relation but at least a triangle of lawyer, hiring group, and ultimate client. The lawyer can no longer single-mindedly consider the interests of his client but must take into account a body of men, some of whom may conflict among themselves. The ideal of service to a single individual is no longer useful as a guide for the lawyer's acts.

If my examples are persuasive in indicating that the individualistic view of the lawyer's function is declining, they might suggest that an increase in personalism is unlikely. The very development of scientific trials and group law might seem to threaten any form of personalism. What evidence supports the belief that a personalist view may become dominant?

Personalism, as here defined, does not permit the client in a trial to ask anything of the lawyer that the lawyer could not conscientiously do for himself. It thus strikes at the shield for personally demeaning conduct, the shield consisting in the belief that vicarious responsibility justifies, or that one may nobly do for another what one would be ashamed to do for oneself. The rhetoric, artifices, and evasions of the old-style trial are instances of what vicarious responsibility permits. Their decline liberates the lawyer to be himself. Free to proceed rationally, the lawyer may be

22 *American Bar Association News*, p. 5 (Feb. 15, 1965).

expected to act as a person, not a tool. He will no longer rationalize his conduct by a doctrine, analogous to *raison d'état*, of "necessity of the client."

Can there be predicted such a development of free, responsible activity that if a lawyer would not defend himself when charged with a crime of which he is guilty, he would refuse to defend a client known by him to be guilty? On the one hand, since it is common practice in the overwhelming number of criminal cases for lawyers to plead guilty clients who are guilty (usually after bargaining), such an absolute standard might not destroy the process of criminal justice. On the other hand, as no one is compelled to incriminate himself, a lawyer might reason that to refuse all clients known by him to be guilty would be to do a disservice to the trial system accepted by society and to create a system in which the lawyer would become in effect a witness for his client's innocence. A sense of personal responsibility by the lawyer would seem to include a respect for the social value of the availability of trials to determine guilt. At all events, with the acceptance of personalism there will be no basis for the lawyers actually conducting criminal trials to permit their clients to use means in which connivance so frequently demeans the advocate.

Moreover, the acceptance of lawyers for groups will provide legal service based on need. The old view encouraged lawyers in charity to give their legal services to the poor, especially in criminal cases, and gradually the Supreme Court made counsel in serious cases a constitutional requirement.[23]

---

[23] The evolution here is from *Powell v. Alabama*, 287 United States Reports 45 (1932) holding that in a capital case involving ignorant, youthful defendants the state had the duty to provide counsel, to *Gideon v. Wainwright*, 372 United States Reports 349 (1963) holding that in all cases where a serious punishment is involved the defendant must be given counsel. Doubtless, evolution here will eventually extend the requirement to cases where the penalty is small.

But the old view failed to stimulate lawyers to give legal service to many poor and middle-income persons who needed it.[24] The new approach will be more effective in providing lawyers to all members of the community, and this quantitative enlargement of the lawyer-using public will be an expansion of legal service to persons.

The development of group law also will have a liberating effect on the lawyer. What will happen is suggested by what sometimes happens now when corporations have wise counsel; here is the one established precedent for the practice of law for a group. The precedent is disguised because the fiction has been maintained that to serve a corporation is not to serve a group but a single entity; the corporation has been imagined as an individual to whose welfare the lawyer's loyalty singly runs. But "corporation" is only an arrangement of certain persons—the chief executive, the directors, the stockholders, the employees. In representing this arrangement of persons a lawyer is representing a group.[25] In the ordinary case the interests of the group are not in open conflict. But where does the lawyer's loyalty lie in case conflict breaks out within the group? Ultimately, it is the stockholders' money that pays him, and orthodox theory on corporations would identify the stockholders as the owners to whom his loyalty is given. Yet in many cases of conflict some of the stockholders are contesting the action of others of the stockholders. In such cases the current prac-

---

[24] See especially Jerome E. Carlin and Jan Howard, "Legal Representation and Class Justice" in Symposium on Group Legal Services in *UCLA Law Review* 12 (1965), 381, and this symposium generally; see also Elliott E. Cheatham, *A Lawyer When Needed* (1963), p. 40; Patricia Wald, *Law and Poverty* (1965), ed. by Abram Chayes and Robert Wald, pp. 64–67.

[25] See *Otis and Co. v. Pennsylvania R. Co.* 57 F. Supp. 680, 681, 684 (E. D. Penn. 1944); *Radiant Burners, Inc. v. American Gas Association*, 207 Federal Reporter Supplement 771, 774 (Northern District of Illinois 1962), *reversed* 320 Federal Reporter 2d, 314 (7th Circuit 1963).

tice is for the lawyer to look to the board of directors representing the stockholders in control at the last election.[26] The lawyer is then conceived of as lawyer for the majority or at least for the group that once had been in control. He is still expected to act with some fairness to the adversary stockholders. In these circumstances it is not unusual for a lawyer to have a certain amount of discretion, to act, within limits, as arbiter of competing forces. The lawyer emerges as a person, whose wisdom determines policy. This emergence is dramatic in the case of conflict, but even in the ordinary pacific situation the interest of the president as employee is not identical with that of the stockholders as investors; the interests of the controlling stockholders do not necessarily coincide with that of all the stockholders; the directors view their work and rewards from a different perspective from that of the salaried employees. In all these instances of submerged conflict, it is the lawyer who today guides the directors, executives, employees, and stockholders to equitable results. It is not because he has a single client, the corporate entity, but because he has an arbiter's sense of justice that the lawyer is able to serve the different persons comprising the group. It may be argued from the generally excellent service that lawyers furnish their corporate clients that men of integrity will be found to do as well for other mixed groups of persons. The expansion of the lawyer's use as arbiter and conscience for a group can only enhance the lawyer's own personality, his awareness of his creative function.

The examples of declining individualism then embody emergent personalism. The personalism of the future will require of the lawyer fuller consciousness of his humanity. The virtue of the lawyer today is justice; the paradigm for

---

[26] See *Marco v. Dulles*, 169 Federal Reporter Supplement 622, 630 (Southern District of New York 1959), *appeal dismissed*, 268 Federal Reporter 2d, 192 (2d Circuit 1959).

his behavior is the court, and its virtue of fairness is his. Yet if the lawyer will not be a tool of a client, neither will he be the simple instrument of justice. Justice is only one of the virtues. There is reason to believe that at one time justice was so hard to attain that lawyers did well to specialize as its defenders. Yet there seems little reason that these specialists, like statues of the goddess, should be forever blinded to other considerations of humanity. There are other virtues besides justice, and to be a human person the lawyer of the future will embody them in his practice of his profession.

Already, in the canons of the American Bar Association, there are glimmerings of the future. However cross his client is at his adversary, a lawyer is not to engage in personalities with opposing counsel: he "should never minister to the malevolence or prejudice of a client in the trial or conduct of a case. . . . Improper speech is not excusable on the ground that it is what the client would say if speaking in his own behalf."[27] What is already a standard of charity in litigation will become the standard in other areas where a lawyer must treat other persons on behalf of his client. Toward all of them, his client's adversaries, victims, creditors, and debtors, he will act with charity. It is now recognized that vicarious responsibility is no excuse for a lawyer's incivility. It will be recognized that it is no excuse for a lawyer's participation in harsh overreaching, avaricious exploitation or disingenuous negotiation. If, as seems likely, harsh, avaricious, or disingenuous clients will have few lawyers to choose from, this result cannot be deplored.[28]

Personalism will profoundly affect one area where now in a special way lawyers act toward some persons as if they

[27] American Bar Association, *Canons of Professional Ethics*, Canon 18.

[28] An exploration of the notion of vicarious responsibility as a defense for uncharitable conduct is made by Curtis, *It's Your Law*, pp. 27–29.

were things. This area is the punishment of crimes. Already the present system is under direct attack. The criticism is as old as Socrates that it makes no sense to do evil to a man to make him better.[29] It has been repeated for our age by the dean of living jurisprudents, Giorgio del Vecchio. He says:

> The truth is, that evil can only be compensated for by good. If the proverb "An eye for an eye, a tooth for a tooth" has been repudiated in its crudest form by the conscience of civilized nations, and one no longer cuts off the hand of a thief or tears out the tongue of a slandermonger, yet the false idea still obtains that the evil of a criminal action must be met with a corresponding evil in its punishment. But does the desire to cause pain to a human being, even though he be guilty, mean that his personality is respected? Or is this not a sort of duplication of the wrong done . . .? Is it just for a human being to be denied the possibility of developing his own spiritual and intellectual powers, and of communicating with his fellow man over long periods of time, even for life? And is it just that such punishment be the motive for grief and serious damage, not only to the culprit, but also to his innocent family?[30]

These sentiments are the sentiments of the present age. They take concrete form in the general decline of capital punishment and in its abolition in eighteen countries and eight American states.[31] Beyond this tangible symptom, it may be speculated that much of the increased sensitivity to the

[29] Plato, *The Republic*, 1. 9. 335 d.
[30] Giorgio Del Vecchio, "Equality and Inequality in Relation to Justice," *Natural Law Forum* 11 (1966), 44.
[31] Clarence H. Patrick, "The Status of Capital Punishment: A World Perspective," *Journal of Criminal Law, Criminology and Police Science* 56 (1965), 397. Thirty-six countries, in addition to those that had abolished the penalty had not had executions in the period 1958–62 covered by Patrick's study (p. 405). He observes: "Actually the yearly total of executions in the world today appears to be less than the number which took place in some single countries at an earlier time." (p. 409).

rights of defendants in a criminal trial results from a sense of unease about the system to which convicted defendants are subjected. In the future, two developments may be expected: prosecutors and judges alike will realize that they are rational agents cooperating in the process by which other men, the criminal defendants, are killed or psychologically injured, that they cannot rid themselves of responsibility by saying that their function is solely to convict or to sentence. At the same time they will recognize that no human person has the right to kill or maim another human person except in self-defense. Retribution may no longer be asserted to be the right of human beings. Nor may a man convicted of a crime be treated as a thing, to be freely used to deter others from criminal behavior.[32] Criminal sanctions then will be seen as possible only as restraints of men actually likely to injure other humans. All other treatment imposed by a court will be genuinely medicinal, directed to rehabilitation in an environment likely to promote rehabilitation. Cooperation will be refused to any system of criminal justice which, giving lip service to rehabilitation, employs measures that can only further disfigure the criminal. The lawyers as participants in the process of criminal law will insist that they not be participants in the denaturing of human beings.

The questions may be raised: Will such a system of personally responsible lawyers be produced? Can it survive? To the first question a confident answer comes only with confidence in the education of lawyers. The lawyers of the future will have had much more formal education than any lawyers of the past. As recently as 1948 only 37 percent of lawyers in practice had college degrees; as recently as

---

[32] See e.g., the demand for reform already advanced in Puerto Rico, Helen Silving, "A Plea for a New Philosophy of Criminal Justice," *Revisto Juridica de la Universidad de Puerto Rico* 35 (1966), 401, 406, 409.

1963, 63 percent had such degrees. It is likely that in another generation 90 percent will have such degrees. Already almost 90 percent of practicing lawyers have law-school degrees as compared to only 61 percent in 1948.[33] If the kind of college education the lawyers receive is broadly humanistic, if the law schools follow the pattern of the leading schools in educating for responsible leadership, it seems probable that the lawyers of the future will have the intellectual resources to be masters of themselves. Any general failure of moral nerve, any general loss of purpose by the culture, must, of course, have its effect on lawyers too; they may, in disbelief in higher values, turn the law into a game for profit or amusement as do many of the lawyers fictionally created by Louis Auchincloss. But there is one factor in the lives of lawyers which will continue to check the easy acceptance of all lack of purpose; they are intimately involved by their work in the realization of human intentions; it is hard for them, though not impossible, to suppose that human creativity is random, chaotic, and without end in view beyond the moment's impulse.

The second question, the viability of a profession composed of such men, requires some consideration of what eats at the present system. One destructive agent is what is preemptively called "corruption" in the way some translators of the Bible preemptively designate sexual sins as "immorality." Corruption in this narrow sense of bribes, favoritism, and profiteering in public office is a major problem of the present. It is least corrosive in the higher judiciary, most corrosive in those areas of administrative action where the government is dispensing favors as small as liquor licenses or as large as television channels. It is unlikely that any governmental system has ever been totally free from

---

[33] American Bar Foundation, *The 1964 Lawyer Statistical Report* 30 (1965).

these evils,[34] and the peculiar dangers of the present rest in the size of the governmental favors available through corruption and the passive acceptance often found toward it. In part, the tolerance extended to it in America is a survival of group thinking at the ethnic tribal level; in part, the tolerance is based on respect for aggressive individualism. Both these bases will disappear. It would be plausible to predict that the self-directing lawyers of the future will be less willing than some client-oriented lawyers today to earn fees as conduits for bribes or influence.

Another class of destructive agents are the bureaucrats. By bureaucrat in this pejorative sense I mean the man who knows all the rules without understanding any of their purposes. He views his job as the mechanical application of whatever his manual prescribes. He presently thrives on the legal staffs of many federal, state, and municipal agencies. He is often a lawyer, but he is the enemy of the true lawyer. It is likely that the creative, purpose-oriented lawyer of the future will effect his radical diminishment.

A third element affecting the present system is its concern with the rich. Probably the best talent of the profession is devoted to the law of the financing, taxation, and regulation of corporations and to the trusts and wills of the wealthy.[35] Even if the assumption is made that those with the most money have the greatest need for legal services, it may be argued that a wider dispersion of legal talent would be healthier. Again, it would seem that the lawyers of the projected future will be more likely to achieve this distribution of services to persons in need.

It may be pressed, however, would lawyers of the kind described be employed? Would they not be such in-

---

[34] See, for example, the many instances of corruption of judges in the Roman Republic and classical Roman Empire, analyzed by John M. Kelly in his book, *Roman Litigation* (1966).

[35] See Cheatham, *op. cit. supra* in 24 at 3.

dependent, nagging, self-willed obstructionists to the realization of entrepreneurial dreams that no one would hire them?
The brusque answer is that, whatever lawyers the future
produces, they will be sought, because business would come
to a standstill without them. Given the present complexity
of governmental regulation and taxation, neither of which is
likely to diminish, lawyers must be used. The kinder, and
no less compelling, answer is that such lawyers already
exist and are far from being shunned: they exist in those
private counselors like Grenville Clark and Harrison Tweed,
who are the consciences of the corporations they serve and
the guiding spirits of many churches, universities, and charitable trusts; in those attorneys in government like Henry
Stimson and Dean Acheson, who invigorated whole depart-
ments of government; in those law professors like Austin
Scott and Warren Seavey, who rationalized and reshaped the
domains of common law they cultivated. The only sound
basis for confidence in the future is to observe that the
present is not without its resplendent representatives.

It is one of the curiosities of Utopian thought to imagine
a world without lawyers as a better world.[36] Lawyers will
always exist in any advanced civilization because human
hopes must be expressed in words, and words are inherently
ambiguous, fragile, open to interpretation and so to argument. Apart from the ambiguity of documents, lawyers are
required by the nature of human problems: in any dynamic
environment, conflicts are not such that one side is always
obviously right; logic and clear ideas are of little help in
resolving them. Resolution comes through argument and
decision, and a lawyer marshals the facts and posits the
values at issue. Resolution comes through compromise, and
a lawyer negotiates it. Resolution comes in advance of con-

[36] Ch. Perelman remarks critically on this phenomenon in "What
a Philosopher May Learn from the Study of Law," *Natural Law
Forum* 11 (1966), 1.

flict, and a lawyer constructs the forms in which human energies are harmoniously channeled. In any real society of opening possibilities, there are tasks that can be done only by the man skilled in words, sensitive to human purposes, knowledgeable of the ways by which human beings are led to cooperate: by the lawyer.

The lawyer will be a participant in the future. It is not, however, Utopian to suppose that the lawyer of the future will be more consciously his own master, less his client's tool; that he will be seeking the truth in disputes; that he will not shelter behind his responsibility for another; that his virtues will not be exhausted by fairness; that he will serve many groups besides the corporation and many persons besides the rich; that he himself will be a charitable creator of values.

12

TECHNOLOGY, BUSINESS
AND EDUCATION

JAMES R. BRIGHT

Graduate School of Business Administration
Harvard University

TECHNOLOGY TODAY is interacting powerfully with business and society and apparently will continue to do so with growing intensity through the foreseeable future. Recent history and current events suggest that technological progress will be the most powerful factor in the future environment for many business firms and other institutions. Although technological change has been with us for many ages and has been a pronounced element in the economic and social environment since the early 1880s, there are at least five reasons why its importance is at present growing.

1. The performance of new technological devices is being improved at a sharply accelerating rate. For example, the atom bomb was thousands of times more powerful than TNT, and the H-bomb was far more powerful than the A-bomb. The first computer had a computing speed two hundred times that of man; recent computers operate many millions of times faster.

2. Successive advances in a given field are introduced more frequently. Consider that, since the coming of the transistor in 1948, there has been a major development in electronic component design about every two and one-half to three years. Each time the industrial leadership and for-

tunes of firms have been severely affected. The tin can was a product that belonged to the steel industry since the days of Napoleon; but, since 1957, the tin can has had at least four new competitors—the aluminum can, the composite fiberboard–aluminum-liner can, the plastic can, and new forms of thin-tin containers. During this time, steel has lost as much as 80 percent of its position in some parts of the tin-container market.

3. The size of the resources needed to bring about many of the new technological innovations (meaning usable hardware and not just the invention itself) is growing to a staggering degree. The U.S. Government spent some two billion dollars to create the atom bomb. IBM is now "betting" more than twice as much—five billion dollars—on their new 360 computer system. And no longer do firms propose the next advance in air transport. The cost is so great that only governments can underwrite the effort. Even consortiums of governments are required, as in the case of the British-French effort to produce the Concorde Mach 2 transport.

4. The impact of new technology on existing institutions is severe and promises to be equally or more severe in the future. Thus, in about twelve years the diesel locomotive wiped out steam locomotive business. In about seven years television played havoc with profits in the movie industry, which is only now struggling back to economic health. In some three years the missile replaced the bomber as the main strategic military weapon. With this replacement went a net loss of close to three hundred thousand jobs in the aviation industry and the displacement of hundreds of thousands of other jobs. Suppliers of equipment, materials, and components had to reorganize drastically. Profitability of many firms fluctuated severely.

5. New technology is creating new communities such as Cape Kennedy, the community around Huntsville, Alabama, and the science-oriented industrial complexes of Boston and

California. New institutions also result, such as NASA, which has a budget larger than almost any other government agency. On the horizon is an oceanographic equivalent of NASA, which will undoubtedly receive similar financial support and result in other new institutions.

New associations also have sprung out of technological progress, such as multination efforts to cooperate in space, to operate communication systems, air transport systems, massive irrigation systems, and water and power distribution projects.

Every institution, corporate and other, faces a high probability that technology will bring a major change to its mode or sphere of work within the next twenty years. The firm, its employees, and its managers inevitably are going to be affected. Technological progress is most assuredly a major element of our world. It is no longer adequate to think of the environment in which we live and work as merely a political, economic, and social environment. This environment now has a technological dimension of increasing significance. Educators dare not neglect this dimension.

The Directions of Technological Progress

Technological change is too broad a notion to be useful, and "automation" is much too narrow to reflect the full technological state of affairs. We must teach ourselves and our children, as well as our institutions, to analyze technological progress for its components and to anticipate the consequences of each type of technological progress. As one such attempt, I offer these eight directions of technical change, with some suggestions of their effects.

INCREASED TRANSPORTATION CAPABILITY

The mastery of distance in less time and/or cost is the result of such devices as the jet transport, the hydrofoil boat, the helicopter, and the less spectacular but very influential developments in container ships, pipelines, piggy-back trailer trains, the unit train, and the superhighway.

Man's ability to move himself and other things has also been affected by resort to new media. Work in space has led to commercial operations—Communication Satellite Corporation—within eight years of Sputnik's launching. Activities under the oceans include such sports as skin diving; and now we see the first two national underwater parks and the beginning of underwater laboratories and submarine tourist activities, such as that which the Swiss operated in Lake Lucerne in 1964, when some ten thousand tourists paid for deep submarine voyages.

INCREASED MASTERY OF ENERGY

Through atomic energy greater magnitudes of power are available for war and peace. Through new control techniques energy is monitored and directed with increased precision. Improved techniques for energy storage, such as nickel-cadmium and other types of batteries as well as fuel cells and nuclear fuel, are making energy portable, divisible, and applicable at very distant points, and on almost any scale. Most striking is the generation and transformation of energy by new sources and devices that did not exist twenty years ago.

INCREASED ABILITY TO ALTER MATERIALS

New properties are given to old materials, making them more durable, stronger, or giving them other special properties. Synthetic materials, especially plastics, are challenging natural materials. Foods and medicines are increasingly being synthesized through industrial chemistry. Progress in materials is changing product design, product life, sources of supply, and therefore the economic health of industries and of regions.

THE EXTENSION OF MAN'S SENSORY CAPABILITIES

Radar and television have broken through limits previously enforced by distance, darkness, and fog. Radio and high fidelity systems, which multiply, amplify, record, and project sound, have expanded beyond measure the ability to speak and hear.

Man's sense of touch has been extended in two ways: (a) his "reach," meaning his ability to control and manipulate things beyond arm's length, has been lengthened indefinitely by progress in remote control, and (b) his power of discrimination has been extended by new instruments for identifying and measuring with minute precision.

The senses of both taste and smell are given new range by chemistry and instrumentation. And it is especially striking that man's memory, meaning his ability to reconstruct what has passed, has been vastly augmented by various types of recording and duplicating mechanisms such as audio-visual tape, magnetic tape for sound, Polaroid photography, and copying techniques such as xerography. Major industries arise around each of these new capabilities.

THE GROWING MECHANIZATION OF PHYSICAL ACTIVITIES

This aspect of automation has been discussed thousands of times (and perhaps overemphasized). It is clear that the mechanization of production tasks will continue. Less appreciated is the entrance of mechanization into the field of distribution. Storing, shipping, and warehousing of goods, order picking, loading of common carriers, and the movement and control of goods passing through the distribution system into the hands of the customer are being mechanized to an ever increasing degree. An integrated, machine-like system is emerging in distribution just as it did in production.

The functions of inspecting and testing also are being

automated, speeding the production process (and incidentally reducing one type of skilled job).

THE GROWING MECHANIZATION OF INTELLECTUAL PROCESSES

This is the other form of automation that has been so widely discussed. Two distinct technical phenomena are involved. The spectacular one is the use of the computer to collect, store, manipulate, and display data or dispatch signals according to its analysis. However, we should not ignore the development of *programming* devices such as magnetic tapes, punched cards, and electronic circuitry. The program control of machine tools, typewriters, and other devices means the direction of long and intricate machinery actions with less human intervention (and less operator skill).

INCREASED CONTROL OF THE ENVIRONMENT

Steady progress is being made in modifying the growth of crops and herds and in controlling their reproduction, their anatomical structures and metabolism, their chemical content, and their usefulness to man's purpose. Organisms also are being adapted to growth in difficult environments. This progress is far from over.

Now we are facing a new activity on a vast scale—the control of temperature, humidity, the chemical content and structure of the water, air, and the types of organic life that will be allowed in the environment.

Environment control is being further realized by the growing ability to alter the earth's surface through techniques of earth moving, dam building, river control, and irrigation. Much of this activity implies infringement on someone else's preferences or property. Political actions thus will affect technological progress to a strong degree.

THE GROWING CONTROL OF HUMAN LIFE

The reduction of disease is an ancient goal, now growing closer. Malaria has almost disappeared; polio is no longer such a terrible threat. We can expect one disease after another to be gradually eliminated.

The second area of technical activity is the increasing ability to control growth, including the generation of life itself. Control of emotions and of body functioning is now commonplace.

It is obvious that we are just at the threshold of major progress in providing mechanical parts for the human body. While artificial limbs are an old story, new versions of artificial kidneys, veins, larynxes, and now the heart itself are accelerating. They will be the basis of significant businesses someday.

Some Economic Consequences

These trends each could be described in greater detail, but for our purpose, what we have noted is enough to suggest the approach we must take and to project the types of effects we can anticipate for economic activity. In the summation that follows, I am withholding judgment on "merits" of continuing technological progress. Let us first simply point out some business consequences and then alert ourselves to some of their social implications.

1. Geography is losing its significance as a barrier to war, to trade, to travel, and to the exchange of cultural ideas and knowledge. A given idea or practice cannot be protected by insulation. Markets and competition will take form at greater distances. It follows that regions of the world will tend to make optimum use of their resources and to specialize in the things they can do best. The barriers to movement are becoming largely political.

2. Therefore, there will be more intense competition between different materials, foods, fuels, transportation systems, and even between recreational areas and different sports. The general trend is increasing competition for every kind of activity. Furthermore, this competition often will come from nontraditional sources.

3. Another kind of competition is growing. I will call this competition through displacement of technological function. Thus, the railroad that hauls coal to power plants finds its business threatened by extra-high-voltage power systems, which make it more economical to ship electricity from the mine mouth than to ship coal to a local power plant. Communications systems providing two-way sight, sound, and facsimile transmission tend to eliminate the need for business travel. Transportation systems are therefore coming into competition with communication systems. Similarly, the speed and cost of transportation are improved, and the need for local warehousing is thereby reduced. The coming of the one-hundred-ton C5A jet freighter will change stock locations and inventory levels. As a material is made corrosion proof, the need for paint is reduced. And in similar manner, many established activities will be eliminated because their functions become unnecessary.

4. The competitive life span of most products will decrease. Technological developments are coming so rapidly that the superior performance of the latest model obsoletes a product far more rapidly than in the past.

5. The cost and time for generating each next major product improvement are increasing.

6. Major industries will arise around each new major technical capability or technological discovery. A prime example is medical activity, which will grow in cost, complexity, and industrial content. The proliferation of special devices and materials in all fields will offer many opportunities for small firms.

7. There will be less and less labor content in carrying out most routine activities, including both production and distribution. Because of a higher machine content, with more capital input required, fixed costs will grow and variable costs decline. The result is that businesses are less able to weather a great variation in demand, especially on the downside.

8. The government is and will be an even greater prime mover in many of these technological advances. In some instances this is because the cost is so great, in others because the government has the need, and in others because it has the span of control necessary. Sometimes the government simply feels the pressure or desire to bring about a major change. Governments, it must be noted, are sensitive to forces that are not always economically rational. Consider how an inflammatory journalistic effort, distorted though it was, forced auto-safety legislation.

9. Many of these technological developments have powerful interactions with other parts of society; *e.g.*, a decision to control water pollution as this decision impinges on towns, communities, individuals, industrial processes, and companies. It follows that we must become sensitive to the "levels of causality" arising out of a technological advance.

10. Because of the variety of technical resources required, there will have to be more consortiums and combinations of companies and institutions to explore and to provide the components needed for technical innovation.

11. There will be more risk and failure in business because of technological uncertainties and technological competition added to the already complex business environment.

12. Technology trends that improve communications, transportation, collection, storage, recall, and display of information will combine to make more and more events and knowledge instantly available from distant points. Education and entertainment will be handled more and more by elec-

tronic-based systems, and the knowledge resources available to every institution and home will grow enormously.

13. Population growth will place great demands on the economy and on society. While food for Americans does not appear to be a problem, the growth of population in developing countries is something else. As Dr. E. E. Howe of Merck Institute for Therapeutic Research recently reported:

> . . . it is useless for our country to institute any program, in a developing country, to increase the food supply without first assuring that there is a major program on population control. To do so will almost certainly increase the sum total of human suffering in the long run.[1]

The anticipated increase of U.S. population to some three hundred million by 2000 A.D. will, however, place us under many other serious economic and social pressures. Transportation, education, medical support, recreation, urban affairs, waste disposal, and many similar areas will be affected. Technology will be called upon to provide solutions.

14. Technology will assure America of more health, wealth in material matters, and vast new industries rising around new technologies; from these, better jobs and economic opportunities will grow.

Social Problems Arising Out of Technological Progress

It is relatively easy to foresee the economic-technological trends and interactions, and it is not too difficult to identify some of the social consequences. But it will take many imaginative and energetic efforts to deal with these problems.

A technological advance, generally, means the creation

[1] E. E. Howe, "World Protein Needs and How They May Be Implemented," *Proceedings* (Washington, D.C.: The Technology of Food Supply, Dairy and Food Industries Supply Association, Inc., 1967).

of superiority and some resulting displacement. Existing devices, products, materials, services, and even industries are superseded by something new. Firms that are blind or inflexible to this type of change will gradually meet economic death. And this means the loss of jobs.

Apparently, and most frequently, new technology builds greater economic activity than it destroys. Whatever jobs aviation might have cost railroading, it has certainly more than made up for by providing as much as twenty times more jobs in building and operating aviation enterprises. Perhaps this is an underestimate. However, as with so much technological change, (1) there is not a one-to-one correspondence between old and new activities; (2) it is almost certain that the new jobs will not be in the same geographic locations; (3) the new technology will not require the same mix of skills and facilities; and (4) there will often be a serious time lag in economic activity while the adjustment is made. While the net effect on total employment throughout society is extremely difficult to state, and undoubtedly will vary from time to time, there is no doubt whatsoever that many individuals will lose present jobs and, thus, that in some manner they must find new ones.

As a corollary, the economic worth of many traditional skills is destroyed because they are no longer needed by society or because a machine does the job faster and better than a person. The destruction of the economic value of existing skills by technological progress is an old, old story in industrial history. Strangely, it has been sadly neglected by many sociologists, labor relations specialists, politicians, and even engineers and managers currently concerned with automation. It is often casually assumed that new and highly complex equipment requires highly skilled *operators*. The opposite is more the case: modern equipment commonly demands of operators almost no skill. A little review of the relative skill required by the modern housewife in contrast to that of her great grandmother is a simple but everyday illustration of the point: many household tasks have been reduced to a matter of reading instructions or pushing buttons. Precisely the same thing has happened with the great bulk (but not all) of industrial jobs as they have become "automated."

However, although *operating* skills frequently are reduced, there is a very distinct increase in the skills (education) required to *design* the new machines and processes and perhaps to perform associated services such as *installation*, *startup*, and *maintenance*. We face the dichotomy of lowering skill requirements in some parts of society and raising them drastically in parts of the planning-designing-controlling-maintaining activities.

Another consideration is simply the number of jobs needed in a new skill. For example, programming of computers was claimed, ten years ago, to require a highly skilled person. With progress in computer languages, and other software, the bulk (but definitely not all) of industry's programming needs can be served by a high school graduate trained in, say, a special two- or three-month programming course. However, the fantastic growth of the computer (now being built at a rate of thirty-five a day by IBM alone, with more than twenty thousand now in use) means that programmers are still in very short supply. Skilled machinists for large, heavy machine tools also are in very short supply because of the sheer volume of demand in certain industries, such as those producing electrical generating equipment.

My purpose is not to insist that a certain end condition will result but only to point out that the effect on skill requirements (and hence education needs) can be quite different in different parts of society, at the same time and because of the same device. We must examine the total mix of effects before we jump into new programs for adjustment.

This leads to the question of the availability of education.

If technological advances are going to come more rapidly, be more severe, and differ widely from what has gone before, it follows that education and reeducation must take place at frequent intervals. The factory worker will need to be taught a new skill. The manager and engineer must acquire a working knowledge of new technology and analytical approaches. Therefore, the need to return to an educational posture from time to time will become more frequent. But American society has not organized its educational institutions to update knowledge and skill in an efficient, systematic, and socially acceptable way. This we must learn to do.

The destruction or decline in the value of assets is another real problem. When a technological advance reduces the value of a given production machine or even a factory, society may be able to accept the disruption without too much upheaval. But when an industry is hit, as when the automobile and airplane destroyed the passenger railroad business or when atomic fuel threatens to reduce coal mining, society has a much more serious problem on its hands.

Some effects on assets are more subtle. They flow out of secondary consequences of a technological advance. How do we respond to the way that the automobile, leading to suburban shopping, may have reduced the value of a downtown store location or a railroad passenger station? And consider the effect of technological progress on the very existence of communities. In California about 40 percent of the wage earners receive their living directly or indirectly from government work in aerospace or defense products. The city of Seattle and its surrounding areas are heavily dependent upon the fortunes of the Boeing Airplane Company.

In the past, regional areas have been badly hurt when their local business has been reduced for economic reasons. It is apparent that now not only may economic factors put an end to given types of activity in a given area, but technological events may also wipe out work. How shall the state or the nation deal with this problem?

Perhaps a wise and energetic government may be able to spur additional economic activity in new fields, but is it possible that these new jobs can be created in factories and industries dedicated to old technology? I think not. It is impossible to provide coal miners with aerospace jobs in coal-mining towns. And this highlights a new need—the *need for mobility*.

Mobility implies that people must be moved into the places where new jobs are available, for new jobs cannot be moved to them very often. Now consider the host of problems that follow from this. First, we have the natural reluctance of people to move from old familiar places and friendly associations. Second, who will provide the cost of relocation and retraining? Must the individual bear this cost? his old firm? his new firm? the new technology? or the government?

Indeed, how shall we find out where new jobs and new skills are needed and match them with skills, or at least aptitudes, of displaced employees? Clearly we need some kind of a national job-information system.

And then what about the continuity of job benefits, and what about attitudes of people who now find no security in years of service and a job well done through a patiently learned skill?

It seems to me that there are two responses that we must structure into our society:

1. We must increase mobility of employees; and this implies knowledge of opportunities, "portability" of job benefits, assumption of retraining and relocation costs, some minimum job security, devices to ease social shock to the family, and probably a change in attitudes. This last point may be the most difficult of all to achieve.

2. We must improve institutions for updating education and providing retraining and new, specialized knowledge

and skill. (This also requires a change in attitudes and procedures toward continuing education.)[2]

One could list a number of other problems growing out of technological progress: as work hours diminish and leisure time grows, where is the virtue in activity? Must we learn a new definition of work?

If constant change, mobility, reeducation, and new locations, activities, friends, and duties can be accepted, what do they do to an individual's life, which now has become highly fragmented? Furthermore, life becomes an activity without roots in places and environments. Does this not do serious damage to the emotional stability of many people?

Let us close with a last concern—the growing gap between the intellectually *élite* and the average worker. It is striking that outstanding managers, scientists, and engineers, and other types of professionals, seem to have an intense interest in their jobs. They are absorbed by them, and they willingly give frantically long hours to "work." Meanwhile, the blue-collar worker seems to get less and less satisfaction out of a more highly automated task. Here he

[2] It is rather interesting to note that the military deal quite successfully with both these problems. Both officers (managers) and workers (enlisted men) move frequently to widely different activities throughout the world. One might argue that they have to take orders. True, but they do not have to spend their careers in such service, as hundreds of thousands choose to do. Why is the military successful in handling mobility? I surmise that it is because (a) *movement is accepted* as part of the job from the moment military personnel are "employed"; (b) moving is *not a financial cost* to the individual; (c) *the receiving community is quite prepared* for the newcomer physically and socially, and (d) *everyone else* in the community is *going and has gone through the same experience* over the years.

On retraining—it is anticipated that the average Army officer spends almost half his career going to schools at various professional intervals. After his basic branch school (*e.g.*, artillery), he can expect, in later years, to attend the Command and General Staff Course (general management), then later the Army War College (policy) or the Industrial College. From time to time he may be tapped for special short courses, such as logistics management, chemical warfare, counterinsurgency, and so on. He readily accepts the notion of continual retraining for new responsibilities and special needs.

has little opportunity to contribute originality of output or differentiation of results. His hours become fewer, more mechanistically controlled, and (I hypothesize) less satisfying. "Work" is something he seeks to reduce. Thus, we are in the peculiar position of reversing the traditional pattern. For the first time in history, workers have free time and sufficient affluence for leisure pursuits, but now the intellectually élite (the professionals) are frantically paced. Shall we deplore the worker's lack of interest in his occupation, or the intellectual's excessive interest in work? There is a disturbing gap here—and a very puzzling one. Moreover, the communication gap between the professional and his family, his employees, and other professionals is growing because of high specialization.

The reader will sense that this little essay has moved from the study of technology to its resulting social problems, and with this shift I for one, have become increasingly less confident of my assessments. Surely, we are leaving future generations of scholars, managers, political leaders, students, and educators ample opportunity to become absorbed in *their* work!

13

DEVELOPING PATTERNS IN PHILOSOPHY

JAMES D. COLLINS
Saint Louis University

P HILOSOPHY IS FULLY involved in the surge of new knowledge and the problems coming in its wake. Quantitative description of the philosophical activity in all countries shows a burgeoning increase of teachers and societies, journals and books, in the period since World War II. The bibliographies of philosophy sponsored by UNESCO and Louvain University have a wide and well-ordered coverage by period and subject matter, but they are unable to record the entire flood of publications in all the specialized areas of interest and are bound to overlook even some outstanding general results. Philosophical societies are organized along national and international lines, in terms of specific periods of thought and special areas of research, and even around individual philosophers of commanding importance or new interest. Predictably, the plethora of meetings, symposia, research programs, editions, and commemorative volumes has resulted in a communications crisis and in some plans for unifying the information flow and achieving a retrieval system. In these respects, the situation in philosophy fits the common description of the rapid expansion of research and communication in the latter part of our century.

Yet just as clearly, philosophy retains its own manner of sharing in the accelerated growth of knowledge. The socialization of philosophical work proceeds according to a distinctive rhythm, determined in part by the close correlation of this work with the other modes of human research and in part by the aims and attitudes of philosophers themselves. The latter are dealing with problems that have a long maturation span, that develop in and through the enlivening diversity of viewpoints, and that require a generalizing judgment about the human significance of the cooperative findings of many minds. And however close and stimulating the integration may be between the philosophical and the other modes of investigation, a certain delaying freedom for reflection and for trying out alternate interpretations is always essential to philosophical study. Perhaps for this reason, it *cannot* be said that over 90 percent of the major thinkers and concepts in philosophy have appeared only in our century. This is not due to an occupational nostalgia for some golden age in the past, or to any disaffection with the advances being made in other fields, or even to a dramatic atrophying of philosophical powers today. Rather, the negative observation serves to underscore that philosophers seek to contribute in their own fashion to the knowledge tide, whose main impact upon philosophical life is more likely to be implosive than explosive in nature.

My aim here is to examine some recent work done in philosophy, in order to discover some patterns of noetic growth that they may manifest. There are three areas in which these patterns will be sought: in historical studies, in the specializing doctrinal fields denominated as "philosophies of" this or that, and in the efforts to achieve some convergence between the general interpretations being offered by phenomenology and analytic philosophy. These domains contain a vast number of findings and embody a number of countertendencies concerning the meaning and goals of philosophy. My limited purpose is to analyze a few out-standing achievements that may well indicate the kind of influence that contemporary philosophical inquiry is having upon the course of mankind. At least it is essential to under-stand that this influence is being determined jointly by the philosophical energies expended in all three fields: historical, special doctrinal, and general interpretative.

The Relevance of History

Like every other theme in philosophy, that concerning the importance of historical studies is open to radical questioning and must be reconsidered in each generation. There was a period (roughly from the mid-thirties of our century until the mid-fifties) when the history of philosophy seemed to be doomed as a creative discipline and element in the formation of the philosophical mind. This was the time when many logical positivists and phenomenologists felt that they could go it alone, that the analysis of common sense and scientific statements or of present attitudes could dispense with historical perspectives, and even that the latter were inhibiting factors to philosophical creativity. This criticism of historical studies was partly a means of overcoming the dominance of idealism which had appropriated history of philosophy for its own ends, and partly a way to foster original thinking against the weight of fact and argument pressing in from the past. Historical research seemed to be incompatible with the new philosophies, both because of its idealistic categories and because of its stifling effect upon any bold thinking in the present.

Although such suspicions are still present in the philo-sophical community, they have had to become adjusted to other considerations that effectively alter the situation. For one thing, there is no need to continue supporting the attitude that historical studies consist in piling up further facts on an already insufferably heavy pile, without discrimination or judgment about their philosophical significance. Like literary critics and artists, the philosophers can take heart from Ben Jonson's remark that we should regard the great minds of the past as guides but not as commanders, as well as from T. S. Eliot's concurring observation that we study the past for fertile comparison and not for the amputation of our own thoughts.[1] Another reason for withdrawing the moratorium on the history of philosophy is that the analysis of human statements and attitudes cannot be carried very far without recognizing that the materials in question convey many levels of significance in an implicit form. A really competent analysis requires that the historical sources of such meanings be investigated and explicitly placed at our disposal. In the study of such historically rooted meanings, neither idealism nor any other philosophy enjoys a monopoly, unless it be that of default through the absence of other working perspectives.

Perhaps the most decisive factor in the new lease upon historical research is simply the actual participation of a significant portion of the philosophical community in such work, as well as the proven usefulness of the research to the rest of us. This is clearly the case with the remarkable developments in the history of Greek thought (especially the research on the pre-Socratic thinkers and on Plato and Aristotle) and in medieval philosophy (a grasp of whose development and continuity is truly a twentieth-century accomplishment), as well as the first steps being taken in East-West comparative philosophy. But I would like to con-

[1] T. S. Eliot, "Tradition and the Individual Talent," in his *Selected Essays* (new ed., New York: Harcourt, Brace & World, 1960), p. 5. The role of history of philosophy is explored by H. R. Smart, *Philosophy and Its History* (Lasalle, Ill.: Open Court, 1962), and by J. H. Randall, Jr., *How Philosophy Uses Its Past* (New York: Columbia University Press, 1963). The effect of the knowledge implosion upon philosophical originality is described by G. J. Seidel, *The Crisis of Creativity* (South Bend, Ind.: University of Notre Dame Press, 1966).

centrate upon three case studies in modern Western philosophy, where we can discern several features of the dynamism of philosophical knowledge in the historical mode. These instances concern skepticism, the Locke-Berkeley complexus, and research on Hegel.

1. A good indication that fresh winds are blowing in the history of modern philosophy is found in the new emphasis being placed upon the role of skepticism. As it was taught a few decades ago, modern philosophy began with some skeptical remarks by Montaigne and their overcoming in the certitude of the Cartesian Cogito, after which no significant role was played by skeptical thinkers. This neat dismissal of the skeptical problem might have satisfied historians of philosophy, had their discipline remained isolated from the rest of the world of learning. But since that discipline was kept deliberately open to other influences, the restriction of skeptics merely to the initial moment of modern philosophizing could not be maintained for very long. For a jarring element was introduced by historians of French culture in the seventeenth century. They noticed that, far from dwindling to a mere rivulet after the criticism of Descartes, the skeptical tradition grew in strength and boldness. From the standpoint of the history of literature and religion, the skeptical movement remained important and kept the initiative, long after 1650. Otherwise, one could make little sense out of Pascal and Bishop Huet, Bayle and the monstrous counterattack on skepticism mounted early in the eighteenth century by Jean-Pierre de Crousaz.

A study of these borderline figures between philosophy and other fields was not enough, by itself, to make a major difference in our way of viewing the early modern years in philosophy. The history of ideas could not transform the history of philosophy solely through its own findings but only by mediation of a philosophical judgment that these findings basically affect our interpretation of some central modern philosophers.[2] The need to take a second look at the skeptical trend became undeniable as soon as it became evident that Descartes, Malebranche, and Leibnitz were much more fundamentally and continually engaged with skeptical issues than was previously suspected. The eventual breakdown of Cartesianism, the difficulties over causality, and the eruption of theodicies and antitheodicies could not be properly understood apart from a more explicit and detailed reference to the skeptical thinkers. Moreover, the full strength of their tradition could be measured only by crossing centennial divisions and geographical lines. Just as skepticism had to be traced backward from Montaigne and into Renaissance Italy, Spain, and Portugal, so did its later fortunes have to be followed into the eighteenth-century Enlightenment in France, Britain, and Germany.[3] To fail to do so would mean losing a basic dimension in our philosophical understanding of Berkeley and Hume, Diderot and Rousseau, Lessing and Hamann. Only when the vital center of pre-Kantian philosophy was seen to be deeply affected by the course of skeptical argumentation, did the cross-fertilization of knowledge from other sources achieve a noticeably different emphasis in the history of modern philosophy.

As often happens, the total effect of this cooperative research is much greater than the summation of the individual projects. For we are now able to recognize the difference between a *distributive* treatment of particular skeptical writ-

---

[2] On the differences between the two disciplines, consult P. O. Kristeller, "History of Philosophy and History of Ideas," *Journal of the History of Philosophy*, 2 (1964), 1–14.

[3] The trend of this research can be followed in: R. H. Popkin, *The History of Skepticism from Erasmus to Descartes* (New York: Humanities Press, 1960); J. S. Spink, *French Free-Thought from Gassendi to Voltaire* (London: Athlone Press, 1960); H. G. Van Leeuwen, *The Problem of Certainty in English Thought, 1630–1690* (The Hague: Nijhoff, 1963); R. A. Watson, *The Downfall of Cartesianism* (The Hague: Nijhoff, 1966); and P. P. Hallie, *The Scar of Montaigne* (Middletown: Wesleyan University Press, 1966).

ings and a *thematic* presentation of the skeptical outlook, as furnishing one of the general and constant motifs in modern philosophy. To seek out the meaning of being and human values, in the presence of a persistent skeptical challenge, is an essential defining note of philosophizing in the modern manner. That is why Hegel treats skepticism as one of the permanent phenomenological formations of the human spirit, why Kierkegaard paradoxically invokes Hume and Hamann together in preparation for the life of faith, why Husserl returns to the Cartesian situation as an archetypal source, and why Santayana weaves his philosophy out of the interplay between animal faith and skepticism. Lucidity concerning the latter's abiding role as a goad to inquiry is a condition for attaining full awareness of the modern philosophical spirit. And in the degree that philosophy is an essential component in man's future, a grasp of the skeptical theme is also a general condition for the attainment of maturity by modern man in his many other cultural modalities.

2. It is always dangerous to say that one has the thought of a past philosopher completely pinned down and dissected. For such an assertion fails to reckon with the nature of historical inquiry, which receives its orientation from *an always changing present situation* in philosophical discussion and in cognate disciplines. What assures our interest in a philosophical source is the proven presence there of pools of meaning, which remain unsuspected or unemphasized until they are found to respond to some current problem in philosophy or some line of research developing in other fields. This delicate correlation between contemporary questioning and the exploration of historical sources is well illustrated by recent studies in Locke and Berkeley, especially their views on science and language. The two topics bearing out this point are best observed when these British thinkers are considered together in dialogue, rather than taken in their separate universes.

A look at the histories of philosophy will show how widely shared was the venerable tradition of dealing with Locke's way of ideas and Berkeley's critique of the concept of matter quite in isolation from the current state of scientific thought. It was considered sufficient to quote Locke's graceful reference to the incomparable Mr. Newton and to hint that Berkeley went in over his depth in his discussion of mathematics and motion. It was possible to retain this attitude of incuriosity about the precise relationship between the two philosophers and the growth of science only up to the time when the nascent disciplines of history of science and philosophy of science began to focus upon the period in question. But then the findings made in these latter areas proved to be so relevant for the better understanding of Locke and Berkeley that a shift of perspective was clearly advisable for historians of philosophy. In turn, their own research is having a reciprocal effect upon the history of science itself, owing to the interlocking relationship among the several disciplines involved.

There is a much broader sharing of concepts and problems (especially on the skeptical issues revolving around knowledge claims about substance and modes) among the continental rationalists and British empiricists than was previously recognized. Yet some definite philosophical differences persist between the two traditions, determined partly by differences in the scientific setting of their respective speculative efforts. It is no more profitable in philosophy than in science to think solely in global terms about the scientific revolution of the seventeenth century. Especially for appreciating the direction taken by British philosophy, it is necessary to distinguish carefully between the pre-Newtonian and the Newtonian phases of scientific thought.

In the main, Locke's fundamental work was done in the pre-Newtonian scientific milieu dominated by Boyle and Sydenham, that is, by experimentalists in the chemical, biological, and medical fields. Hence the *Essay Concerning Human Understanding* made a uniquely tempered synthesis between the interpretative activities of reason and attention, the dynamism of the material world, and the restricted range of our knowledge.[4] Diagnostic probability was assigned a large role in both theoretical and practical issues, thus giving Locke a middle path between systematic rationalism and skepticism. Perhaps only on the eve of Newton's triumph was it possible to attain precisely this blending of epistemological factors and to regard it as a satisfactory solution of the issues.

To view Berkeley as coming in the wake of the *Principia* and indeed in the full tide of the Newtonian popularizers is to realize that his intellectual position is something more than a conceptual *tour de force*. He is not simply drawing paradoxical conclusions from statements made by Locke but is wrestling with changes induced by Newton's conception of natural philosophy and the contributions made to it by mathematics and experiment. Yet we have been able to grasp Berkeley's problem only as a result of the confluence of three factors in the current growth of knowledge: the editing of his own early *Philosophical Commentaries;* the comparisons, made by philosophers of science, between Berkeley and Ernst Mach on the constructive and interpretative elements embodied in scientific laws; and the aforementioned prolonga-

---

[4] The Lockean synthesis of science and epistemology is the central theme in two books: C. A. Viano, *John Locke: Dal razionalismo all' illuminismo* (Turin: Einaudi, 1960), and Maurice Mandelbaum, *Philosophy, Science, and Sense Perception* (Baltimore: Johns Hopkins Press, 1964). Special aspects of this correlation are studied in a remarkable series of articles published in *Journal of the History of Ideas:* R. M. Jost, "Locke's Rejection of Hypotheses About Submicroscopic Events," 12 (1951), 111–30; D. A. Givner, "Scientific Preconceptions in Locke's Philosophy of Language," 23 (1962), 340–54; P. Romanell, "Some Medico-Philosophical Excerpts from the Mellon Collection of Locke's Papers," 25 (1964), 107–16; G. A. J. Rogers, "Boyle, Locke, and Reason," 27 (1966), 205 16; L. Laudan, "The Nature and Sources of Locke's Views on Hypotheses," 28 (1967), 211–23.

tion of studies of skepticism into the British sphere. Only when they are all drawn together do these lines of investigation enable the historian of philosophy to make a more appreciative reading of the text of Berkeley. His immaterialism is now seen to be, not a wild Gaelic fancy, but a shrewd and well informed attempt to defend a minimal coherence of thought and language at a time when the Newtonian world picture was providing further grist for the skeptical tropes.

On a closely related issue, our conception of Locke and Berkeley is being modified in the light of another contemporary focus of scholarship. This time, the revision is stimulated by the joint implications of language studies and the linguistic approach in philosophy of science. These tendencies make the historian of philosophy specially sensitive to a deficiency in his treatment of the two British thinkers, namely, his relative slighting of their remarks on the nature and functions of language. The linguistic turn in philosophy is having deep repercussions on the entire history of philosophy, making a prime topic of the doctrine on language in all the historical sources. Berkeley is a clear beneficiary of this new interest. In the course of exorcizing all meaning from the term "matter" and of bringing everyday usage in line with his immaterialist outlook, he becomes quite reflective on the several uses of language. He examines its role not only in communication of theoretical knowledge but also in evocation of moods, in persuasion of assent, and in the fine tactics of obfuscating another mind. As for Locke, his correlation between words and representative ideas by no means constitutes the sum of his theory of language. To appreciate its real complexity, however, this theory must be studied in conjunction with his account of active reflective reason and his scientific preconceptions.

Both literary critics and comparative philosophers are interested in the dominant metaphors that distinguish one art work or one philosophical standpoint from another. Until recently, analysis in terms of the distinguishing root metaphor was applied mainly to broad philosophical positions and concepts, such as hylemorphism, monism, and organicism. But this approach is now being extended to the study of individual thinkers, including Locke and Berkeley. Both men are dissatisfied with the metaphor of the machine as a model upon which to organize their reflections about the knowing process and the nature of the universe.

Without fully anticipating Dewey, Locke the medical man and civil servant does modify the mechanistic account of knowledge by viewing the relation of man to the world in more organic and practical terms. In a living, practical intercourse with the world, man does not have to claim that his definitions give a sharply etched and essential insight into the nature of things. It is by subordinating the machine metaphor to a more humane one, drawn from the practice of the chemist, the physician, and the statesman, that Locke is enabled to describe with equanimity the flickering candle of practical human intelligence at work in the world of everyday affairs.

In Berkeley's case, the machine metaphor is not only subordinated but replaced by the metaphor of language itself.[5] Since he is not encumbered by a theory of ideas as representatives of states of matter, he can establish a direct relationship between ideas, or sensible things, and the realm of mind. Berkeley conceives of the pattern among the ideas constituting nature to be a kind of language: it is the manner in which God communicates His presence to men, and which

[5] A full scale interpretation of Berkeley in terms of the plurality and elusiveness of the metaphors required for understanding the natural world is made by C. M. Turbayne, *The Myth of Metaphor* (New Haven: Yale University Press, 1962). The function of metaphors in scientific thinking is set forth historically by T. S. Kuhn, *The Structure of Scientific Revolutions* (Chicago: University of Chicago Press, 1962), and in logical terms by M. B. Hesse, *Models and Analogies in Science* (South Bend, Ind.: University of Notre Dame Press, 1966), especially pp. 157–77.

enables men in turn to acknowledge the divine reality in their practical activities. Instead of being an autonomous machine, remorselessly grinding out its operations and frustrating our efforts to relate with it, the sensible world is to be viewed as a divine-human linguistic pattern. Its function is sacramental and expressive: to manifest the reality of the divine spirit to men and to give orientation to the tendencies of the human spirit in its search for interpersonal values.

What these researchers in Locke and Berkeley suggest is that our comprehension of modern philosophers will be increased by making a twofold comparison, as a matter of deliberate policy. We should try to illuminate a particular philosophy by examining the *scientific matrix* within which it develops, and also by looking for its *guiding metaphor* on how to conceive the universe and man's function therein. As the instance of the British empiricists shows (and this theme could be pursued in Hume's imaginative variation of mechanical and organic models of the world), the reflective originality of a philosopher vis-à-vis the predominant scientific conception of things is often discovered in his use of a slightly different central metaphor than the one underlying the scientific theorizing. In long range terms, the example of Locke and Berkeley also suggests that the philosophical component in the growth of human knowledge will continue to be closely responsive to the current phase of scientific thought and yet remain somewhat critically related to it. One facet of the philosophical vocation is to keep searching for more adequate metaphoric guides than the reigning one. This methodic dissatisfaction furnishes one intellectual condition enabling both the philosopher and the scientist to make further creative advances beyond a given state of research. To resist the sealing-off process of a ruling world view (whether picturable or not), there must be an opportunity for philosophical self-interrogation as well as for scientific hypothesizing.

3. As late as thirty years ago, it would have been a safe prediction that Hegel would lose his power of fascination for the philosophical community and that investigations into his thought would dwindle to an inconsequential trickle, more philological than philosophical in import. And yet the present horizon is filled with research works and popularizations, journals and congresses (in both Eastern and Western Europe), dedicated to Hegel's philosophy. In scope, intensity, and competence, this new tide of interest is unsurpassed by previous contributions in that area.[6] The renascence of Hegelian studies is a cautionary lesson that no historical assessment, especially a negative judgment of obsolescence, concerning a major philosophical mind can be regarded as utterly definitive. More than likely, such a judgment means, not that the primary source itself has run dry and lost all attraction for men, but that a particular line of interpretation of the primary source has now petered out. New methods of releasing the intellectual riches have to be devised, but the history of philosophy is like that of literature insofar as there is never a total abandonment of the effort to reawaken the primary texts.

In examining the phenomenon of Hegel's rebirth among us, we can at the same time improve our self-comprehension. There was no arbitrary way in which an enthusiast could convince people about Hegel's actual relevance. That evaluation could result only from a remarkable convergence of many directions of inquiry upon a common focus in the thought of Hegel.

One such contemporary motivation rises from the world-wide need to understand the intellectual roots and genesis of

[6] Hegel research is reported extensively in *Hegel-Studien* (1961 ff.). Its international character, correlation with many fields, and philosophical sweep, are evident from three symposia: "Studies in Hegel," *Tulane Studies in Philosophy*, 9 (1960); D. C. Travis, ed., *A Hegel Symposium* (Austin: University of Texas Press, 1962); "Hegel Today," *The Monist*, 48 (1964), 1–132.

Marxism.[7] Unavoidably, the effort to grasp the outlook of Marx, especially as expressed in his humanistically oriented early economic-philosophic manuscripts, leads men back to a fresh reading of Hegel. The ambiguity of the Right and Left Hegelian schools invites scholars to trace that ambiguity to its fountainhead and thus to make a more humanistic and work-centered interpretation of Hegel. Especially the Hegel of the *Phenomenology of Spirit* and *Philosophy of Right* shows a modern awareness of social strife and historical development of attitudes which is useful not only for appreciating Marxism but also, more directly, for grasping the conflicts and aspirations of our developing century.

The reappraisal has gathered further momentum from the effective use of the Hegelian heritage made by existentialists and phenomenologists. They have dissociated the idea of dialectical method from the construction of a ponderous system and restored it to the function of discerning the formation and interplay of complex meanings within the self and in society. In so doing, they have brought into relief the twin Hegelian themes of freedom and concrete thinking.[8]

[7] The Hegel-Marx relationship looms large in: A. Cornu, *The Origins of Marxian Thought* (Springfield, Ill.: C. C. Thomas, 1957); R. Garaudy, *Dieu est mort: Étude sur Hegel* (Paris: Presses Universitaires, 1962); K. Löwith, *From Hegel to Nietzsche* (New York: Holt, Rinehart & Winston, 1964); J. Hyppolite, *Études sur Marx et Hegel* (new ed., Paris: Rivière, 1965); N. Rotenstreich, *Basic Problems of Marx's Philosophy* (Indianapolis: Bobbs-Merrill, (1965); L. Dupré, *The Philosophical Foundations of Marxism* (New York: Holt, Rinehart & Winston, 1966); and S. Avineri, *The Social and Political Thought of Karl Marx* (New York: Cambridge University Press, 1967).

[8] These topics dominate the expert general presentations made by J. N. Findlay, *Hegel: A Re-Examination* (New York: The Macmillan Co., 1958); W. Seeberger, *Hegel oder die Entwicklung des Geistes zur Freiheit* (Stuttgart: Klett, 1961); and G. R. G. Mure, *The Philosophy of Hegel* (New York: Oxford University Press, 1965). A good place to begin the study of cultural and moral alienation is in these works: Findlay, pp. 119–31; Seeberger, pp. 416–45; Mure, pp. 93–102. Also A. W. Levi, "Existentialism and the Alienation of Man," in *Phenomenology and Existentialism*, ed. by E. N. Lee and M. Mandelbaum (Baltimore: Johns Hopkins Press, 1967), pp. 243–68.

These themes are never properly developed within the extreme settings of individualism and totalitarianism. For Hegel, the achievement of human freedom and concrete values is essentially a social and interpersonal task, one that sets goals for society in the very act of maturing the quality of personal intelligence and decision. This is one reason why the existentialist and phenomenological analyses are pitched at the intersubjective level. To penetrate the human situation, these analyses must respect our essential openness to the world, temporality, and social history. Hegel's actuality can be measured by his influence in determining these latter points of reference for the study of man.

We also come to acknowledge Hegel's germinating presence whenever we probe into the historical springs of the basic themes of *alienation* and the death of God. Here is a striking confirmation of the claim that philosophy has its own rhythm of maturation and that several disciplines usually contribute to the process as soon as human nature in its broadest aspects is involved. From his earliest manuscripts to his most finished treatises, Hegel's writings are filled with a sense of the dislocations in the psyche and society. He develops a theory of man's alienation and thingification—his loss of spiritual self-possession and union with natural processes— as a means of interpreting such universal phenomena in our lives. One of the chief expressions of alienation is found in the feeling that we are cut off from the divine life and that, in fact, God is no longer a living actuality among us.

But it has taken a century and a half for these thoughts to seize hold upon our general outlook. For this widespread awareness of the implications of alienation to grow, much more has been required than the philosophical reflections of Feuerbach and Marx, Nietzsche and Sartre. Their leading ideas have had to be integrated with the specific work done on the problem in the framework of psychiatry and theology, sociology and literary criticism. What we now call the pervasive sense of alienation is a complex and slowly developing signification and practical attitude. Into its formation and elucidation have gone the joint efforts of men working in all these fields, with their appropriate methods and concepts.

One of these co-contributing disciplines is the history of philosophy, which does not specify its activities in a cultural vacuum. In serving the needs of philosophical reflection, it also serves the broader demands of humanity in our age. The historical findings on the philosophical sources of the themes of alienation and God's death are being put to many uses by scholars and reflective minds of all sorts. This is a sure sign that we have only started to plumb these interpretations of our existence and to make them somehow operative in our social and religious life. Our future relationships with our fellow men and God will be deeply marked by our prolonged experience and examination of alienation in all its modes.

Into the Special Fields

A characteristic tendency among many philosophers today is to dedicate oneself to some special doctrinal field. Whereas a Kant or a Hegel dealt with art, religion, and history as parts of a general systematic investigation, some philosophers are now inclined to concentrate their entire inquiry in one of these regions. The philosophy of science is so vast and complex an enterprise that the individual thinker feels barely able to keep abreast with its main currents and to contribute to some specific issues. Owing to the vast influx of materials, the philosopher of art finds generalization difficult within the world of art, let alone the achievement of integration with the rest of philosophy. Moreover, there are journals and associations, technical vocabularies and research instruments, devoted exclusively to the philosophy of history or the philosophy of religion. The pressures of research and competency often induce a man to restrict his professional work to but one of these worlds of meaning, even though he has to abandon the traditional image of the philosopher as one who maintains a universal concern for the problems of mankind.

Thus it would be misleading to depict philosophers as a uniform group of partisans of generality confronted with the world of specializing tendencies in all other sciences and arts. Philosophy is thoroughly a member of this world of knowledge increasing through the pathways of specialization, and hence it experiences at its own intimate center the tension between a general humane concern and the drive toward specialized types of research and judgment. Yet it belongs within this world of accelerating research in its own way and has its own way of responding to the internal tug toward *both* general wisdom and specializing competence. Since it belongs to the philosopher's vocation to become as reflective as possible about his condition and methods of work, it may be instructive to examine some features of this domestic tension in philosophy today. The manner in which philosophers are meeting this problem may have some analogical significance for other investigators as well.

Instead of approaching this question directly from the standpoint of the philosophical generalist in methodology and theory of knowledges, however, I would like to show how the question formulates itself within the perspective of the philosophical specialist himself. This can be conveniently observed in the philosophy of history, although some adjustments would be required to fit other areas of special doctrinal speculations. And in order to grasp the operative pattern, it is advisable to focus upon the common conditions and tendencies of the work being done in this field of philosophy of history, rather than upon individual motivations.

There is a significant absence of a wall of isolating indifference between the working historian and the philosopher of history. The two manage to maintain an operational zone of interrelation, not indeed between history and philosophy taken in block form, but rather between certain mutually relevant phases of active discussion in these two disciplines. This *phasic operational* relationship is one of the firm, actual modes of communication found in our universe of rapidly separating galaxies of knowledge.[9] Some professional historians regard it as important for their research and the formation of students to consider general questions about the meaning of history and the nature of historical knowledge, just as some philosophers deem it necessary to specify their own treatment of these same questions by a study of the actual practice of historians. An added inducement toward gaining mutual clarification exists because persuasive interpretations of history and historical judgment have already been introduced into the public forum by a Voegelin and a Toynbee, neither of whom can be categorized strictly as a historian or as a philosopher of history. Thus one valuable area of intersection among the knowledges of man is being supported by the recognition of some common interests and problems among otherwise differently orientated investigators.

However, diverse their theoretical positions, philosophers of history agree in practice today upon a very broad threefold division of their problems. Most philosophical discussion can be grouped around the three areas of internal patterns and trends in history, the nature of historical statement and expla-

9 This interchange is encouraged by the examples of a philosopher (B. Croce) doing professional historical work and of a historian reaching a reflective generalization about his field (E. H. Carr, *What is History?* [New York: Alfred A. Knopf, 1962]). The open door policy prevailed at the conference for historians and philosophers presided over by Sidney Hook: *Philosophy and History* (New York: New York University Press, 1963), as well as in two philosophical anthologies: *Theories of History*, P. Gardiner, ed. (Glencoe: The Free Press, 1959), and *The Philosophy of History in Our Time*, H. Meyerhoff, ed. (New York: Doubleday Anchor, 1959). This cooperation is placed upon a permanent editorial footing in the journal *History and Theory*.

nation, and the relationship between such pattern and explanation and the basic historicity of man.[10] Although there is a close connection between these three types of philosophical theory of history, they do help to define different aspects of the meaning of history and even of the philosophical work being done in this field. Roughly speaking, the contributions of the classical tradition of philosophers of history from Vico and Hegel to Comte and Dilthey center around the speculative determination of patterns and trends; recent Anglo-American inquiry is concerned mainly with the critical and methodological analysis of historical explanation; and the phenomenological and existential stress is laid upon the anthropological aspect of history, as expressive of our historical mode of being. This division is one of emphasis rather than of exclusive interest, since most philosophers of history refuse to take a narrowly reductive view of the tasks in their field, whatever restrictions they may place upon their personal range of work.

Looking now at the problem of doctrinal specialization from within the threefold structure of the theory of history,

---

[10] W. H. Walsh's *Philosophy of History* (New York: Harper Torchbook, 1960) and B. Mazlish's *The Riddle of History* (New York: Harper & Row, 1966) exploit the first two categories: the speculative theory of the meaning and mechanism of history, and the critical theory of how we come to know what happened. The third approach in terms of philosophical anthropology and transsubjective time is developed metaphysically in three groundbreaking books: N. Rotenstreich, *Between Past and Present* (New Haven: Yale University Press, 1958); E. L. Fackenheim, *Metaphysics and Historicity* (Milwaukee: Marquette University Press, 1961); Paul Weiss, *History Written and Lived* (Carbondale: Southern Illinois University Press, 1962). From the phenomenological and existentialist side, one may consult: Edmund Husserl, *Phenomenology and the Crisis of Philosophy* (New York: Harper Torchbook, 1965); Karl Jaspers, *The Origin and Goal of History* (New Haven: Yale University Press, 1953); Karl Löwith's two works, *Meaning in History* (Chicago: University of Chicago Press, 1949), and *Nature, History, and Existentialism* (Evanston, Ill.: Northwestern University Press, 1966); and Paul Ricoeur, *History and Truth* (Evanston Ill.: Northwestern University Press, 1965).

we can see that there is no sheer closure of this specialized field. In the degree that a contemporary philosopher of history draws sustenance from the previous philosophical tradition, he recognizes the powerful continuity between the general theories of knowledge, action, and value in a Kant or a Hegel and their respective treatments of progress and freedom in history. Reflection upon such a correlation between the broad philosophical framework and the specific conception of historical trends and patterns in these classical instances is a spur toward making explicit whatever similar correlation may be used by today's specializing philosopher of history. A scrutiny of his own operative presuppositions not only makes his treatment of history more straightforward and rigorous but also keeps it permanently open to the integrating principles and to the other specific domains in philosophy, in the degree that their relevance to his procedures can be shown.

The fact is, however, that much contemporary theorizing about history moves from the first-level study of patterns to the second-level study of the kinds of statement and explanation that yield historical knowledge. This shift of interest to the epistemology and methodology of historical discourse (from discourse *in* the historical mode to that *about* the historical mode) is not an isolated phenomenon peculiar to workers in the field of philosophy of history. It corresponds to a more general trend toward an analytic study of groups of statements made in several modes of discourse: scientific and esthetic, moral and religious. Here is another indication that the philosopher of history is not so lost in his specialization that he does not respond to, and make effective use of, methodic approaches working more generally throughout the regions of philosophy.

We have a case here of that sort of specialization which does not sunder all relationships with the rest of philosophy. This is evident from the treatment of even some quite specific issues. For instance, differences concerning the use of causal language in historical explanation can be traced to some general differences among philosophers over the nature of the causal relationship, the need for adaptation to human action as a subject matter, and the comparison between scientific and historical description of the course of events. Far from being a sealed-off compartment, the philosophy of history often serves, along with the philosophy of science, as a testing ground for the explanatory reach of a general theory of knowledge and reality.[11] Just as there is open intercourse between positions taken in philosophy of science and those taken in the theory of historical statements, so is there a channel of communication between these zones of inquiry and and the central themes in any philosophy of human experience.

The purpose of contemporary metaphysical and phenomenological studies of history is precisely to explore this fundamental channel and to make it an actually traveled route for understanding the meaning of history. That meaning is not exhausted by determining some internal trends within the historical process and some structural limits of statements and acts of comprehension concerning such process. We also have the opportunity of following these two approaches to their point of unification in human reality and, hence, of inquiring how it is that we live historically and engage in historical inquiries at all. To ask about the historical nature of human existence and thinking in this general way is to

[11] The complementarity between theory of knowledge and theory of history can be seen in three analytic works: P. Gardiner, *The Nature of Historical Explanation* (London: Oxford University Press, 1952); W. H. Dray, *Laws and Explanation in History* (London: Oxford University Press, 1957); A. C. Danto, *Analytical Philosophy of History* (New York: Cambridge University Press, 1965). Carl Hempel's application of his philosophy of science to historical explanation is a central point for discussion in the essays edited by W. H. Dray: *Philosophical Analysis and History* (New York: Harper & Row, 1966).

bring the philosophy of history explicitly within the matrix of one's central philosophy of man in relation to his world. It is to raise the question of the distinction between the temporality and historicity of nature and that of the specifically human mode of existing in natural reality. Such generalizing of the interpretative basis of history is not the privilege of any one school of philosophy, even though at present it is cultivated most steadily by the phenomenologists and existentialists. One task for future dialogue is to stake out the common ground that these philosophical approaches occupy along with the Marxist, naturalist, and idealistic conceptions of man's temporality and historicity.

As it turns out, then, the philosophy of history provides a meeting place for diverse intellectual interests. It evokes a flow of phasic operational communication between historians and philosophers; it furnishes a challenge to general theories of method and knowledge to test themselves in a concrete portion of human life; it offers a significant variation of problems for workers in the theory of science or art or religion; and it encourages the different philosophies of man and nature to compare their accounts of how the historical mode of being develops within the natural world. A regional theory that includes such generalizing functions within its proper scope is not actually opposed to the philosopher's vocation of seeking wisdom but provides one path toward obtaining wisdom within the context of our world of expanding knowledge. It is not the prelude to fragmentation, but rather it generates a new integrating level of human cognition and values.

This suggests that the trend toward specialization in philosophical studies should be viewed in function of the life of *the entire philosophical community*. As Charles Peirce once remarked, philosophy no less than science profits from the modern requirements of the division of intellectual labor. This or that individual line of motivation may be quite separatist and isolationist, but the impact of the specialized work as a whole responds to a more open and integrating spirit. The healthy growth of the philosophical community requires that intensive efforts be made to penetrate each area of human activity, to master the methods used in each field, to show the need for adaptation and analogical application of all general principles of method, knowledge, and being, and thus to generate a constant interflow of philosophical intelligence between the foundational and the specializing types of inquiry. Without imposing its own pattern upon the other arts and sciences, philosophy can offer some encouragement to the specialist that he is not tearing the world asunder, and to the generalist that he is not committed to an airy realm of unity devoid of the hard diversities of life.

The Phenomenological and Analytic Convergence

It is a widely acknowledged trait of philosophy since the midcentury that well-planned efforts are being made to break through the barriers separating the two most widespread positions—phenomenology and analytic philosophy. They can no longer be assigned to different geographical homes, since in America at least there is a growing acquaintance with the phenomenological method and source materials, while conversely several continental thinkers are making good use of the analytic and linguistic procedures. As a result of such mutual explorations, it has been found that the two traditions share many more problems and basic concepts than was originally suspected. Since this pattern of convergence is likely to become more pronounced in the coming years, it is fitting to conclude the present analysis of basic patterns with four considerations relevant to the tendency in question. They concern the meaning of convergence, the contribution of historical studies to this tendency, the contribution to it made by some specific doctrinal topics, and the image of the philosopher which emerges from the whole process.

1. It is important to retain the distinction between a

movement of *convergence* and one of *identification*. There are no indications that analytic and phenomenological philosophies are being related in such fashion as to bring about their ultimate fusion and identification. This would be a goal of questionable worth in any case, since it would entail the rubbing-out of certain differences that enable thinkers to perceive different meanings and values, all of which must be cultivated by mankind. Instead, the convergence tendency has a restricted, yet quite important, aim that can be expressed in negative terms and then in more positive ones.

The negative goal is to remove entirely the stultifying preconception that only one of these approaches incorporates a genuine philosophic method and that the other one is the expression of some extraphilosophical cultural condition. The general applicability of the one philosophic method does not necessarily entail the reduction of the other to the status of being either a latent variation of the first or else a psychic and cultural condition, requiring a technique of therapeusis rather than argumentation. Since both the analytic and the phenomenological methods are characterized by their quite general range of operation and by the use of therapeutic techniques, a rather severe intellectual self-disciplining is required for removing the exclusivist imputation. This means that the discovery of elements of similarity between the two philosophical procedures is not to be construed as building the case for their eventual identification or for the total subordination of the one to the other.

More positively expressed, once the two philosophies are brought within hailing distance and encouraged to enter discussion on the footing of mutual integrity, then the differences can be recognized and encouraged. Each one will retain its own manner of achieving rigor and experiential content. Philosophers within the two traditions can learn to converse together and accept insights from each other, without permitting the conversation to become transformed into a total merger and blurring of distinct perspectives.[12] If this meaning for philosophical convergence is appropriate for the relations between analysts and phenomenologists, then it may also guide us in the far more complicated task of strengthening the philosophical discussions between East and West.

2. A further point of relevance for the previously considered work of historical investigations can now be established, namely, the bearing of historical studies upon the phenomenological-analytic convergence. The potentialities for convergence contained in the historical order are only now beginning to be realized, and we may expect that this instrument for broadening the basis of philosophical communication will be used with increasing effectiveness. Its likely fruits can be predicted by indicating just one line of pertinent research, that concerned with Husserl's central concept of intentionality.

Whenever Husserl himself recounted the historical origins of the theme of the intentional directedness of human acts to an objective world, he acknowledged a special debt to Descartes and Brentano, Hume and Kant. Considerable attention has been paid to his first two predecessors on this topic, but at least in the English-speaking world his relationship *with*

[12] An opening toward the values in Continental philosophy is detectable in two cooperative volumes: *Clarity Is Not Enough*, H. D. Lewis, ed. (New York: Humanities Press, 1963), and *British Analytical Philosophy*, ed. by B. Williams and A. Montefiore (New York: Humanities Press, 1966). The editors of the latter work call attention to "the development of a certain underlying tension in contemporary British philosophy. On the one hand, the mood and intent are still predominantly empiricist; on the other hand, the implications of many of the methods used and of the insights attained are not but are moving in a phenomenological and even a metaphysical direction" (pp. 6–7). Conversely, there is an opening toward British and American traditions from the side of phenomenology, as testified by two further collections: *Realism and the Background of Phenomenology*, R. M. Chisholm, ed. (Glencoe: The Free Press, 1960), and *An Invitation to Phenomenology*, J. M. Edie, ed. (Chicago: Quadrangle Books, 1965). In the same spirit, see the issue of *The Monist*, 49 (1965), 1–164, devoted to "Linguistic Analysis and Phenomenology."

Hume and Kant on the constitution of objective meaning has not been sufficiently emphasized.[13] And yet it is precisely from a historically enlightening comparison with the two latter thinkers that we can measure the depth of Husserl's engagement with the same basic problems and sources nourishing the analytic tradition and thus that we can hope to remove the aura of strangeness still persisting around him. The Husserlian doctrine of intentionality is one way of responding to Hume's question of how we can maintain the identity of a perceptual object, amid all its variations and in the face of so much incompleteness of actual perception. And it is also a response to the difficulties engendered by Kant's attempt to account for the objectivity of statements in the scientific, moral, and esthetic modes of discourse. Historical probing into these roots of the problem of intentionality shows that there is a much closer confrontation of the same abiding issues of perception and reasoning, plurimodal discourse and the human context, than the cultural, terminological, and temperamental differences between twentieth-century phenomenologists and analytic thinkers would initially suggest.

A better understanding of the development of American philosophy is promoted also by a broadened historical study of intentionality. This is not surprising in view of the common sources studied by Husserl and the generation represented by William James, Royce, and Peirce. All these men

---

13 A good start can be made by consulting the accounts of intentionality given in: H. Spiegelberg, *The Phenomenological Movement* (2nd ed., 2 vols., Hague: Nijhoff, 1965), 107–17 (with references to William James); Q. Lauer's two books, *Phénoménologie de Husserl: Essai sur la gènese de l'intentionnalité* (Paris: Presses Universitaires, 1955), and *The Triumph of Subjectivity* (New York: Fordham University Press, 1958); and Aron Gurwitsch's influential *Studies in Phenomenology and Psychology* (Evanston, Ill.: Northwestern University Press, 1966), pp. 124–74 (valuable comparisons of Husserl with Hume and Kant). It would help to have in English a thorough analysis of Husserl's relations with Hume and Kant, comparable to Iso Kern's *Husserl und Kant* (The Hague: Nijhoff, 1964).

had to wrestle with the theories of Hume and Kant concerning the relationship between the surging life of consciousness and the objective meanings that develop and persist in our world. Both the German thinker and the Americans were also sensitive to the radical psychologism proposed by Mill and Wundt, as well as to several forms of evolutionary and historicist explanation of the human mind in bio-causal terms.

As we increase our historical understanding of these shared sources, we can better appreciate why James should do more than write another version of German laboratory psychology.[14] He engaged in a phenomenological search for the sedimented meanings incorporated in our everyday experience and in scientific concepts, as well as for the persistent aims of man the agent and evaluator, who organizes his several worlds of meaning. Royce (who read Fichte early in life and Husserl in later life) elaborated his own theory of intentionality, relating human meanings to the will activity of an absolute center of life and thought. For him as well as for Husserl, an intimate bond holds between intentional activity and the human self's existence in a community rather than in a solipsistic shell. Peirce also bore the marks of a thinker who had delved into the same sources as had Husserl. He focused on the patterned growth of the community of scientific investigators as one major form of intentional activity and was just as concerned as Husserl to show that such activity is more ultimate than the Cartesian notes of clarity and distinctness of evidence.

3. The tendency toward intellectual convergence, but not coalescence, among the philosophical traditions of our century receives increasing impetus from the philosophical study of *language*. Until now, the phenomenological and the analytic

---

[14] See Gurwitsch's essay, "William James's Theory of the 'Transitive Parts' of the Stream of Consciousness," in *Studies in Phenomenology and Psychology*, pp. 301–31, as well as J. M. Edie's essay, "Notes on the Philosophical Anthropology of William James," in *An Invitation to Phenomenology*, pp. 110–32.

examinations of the language phenomenon have been con-
ducted in quite separate cubicles. This is understandable,
owing to the great complexity of the subject, the many ramifications it has within a particular philosophy, and the rapidity
with which general linguistics has developed. In addition,
one's own language and literature provide such a rich source
of reflection that one's philosophical horizon can easily be
made coterminous with them. As a consequence, the two
philosophies have followed separate paths in their investigation of language. But there are some factors presently at
work which make it difficult to convert a situation of factual
separation into a principle of isolation or even into an evalua-
tive judgment about work done elsewhere. Hence such comparative factors are potent means of opening the cubicles and
encouraging some cooperative research.

The strong emphasis upon linguistic topics within the
analytic group has had the good effect of compelling contemporary phenomenologists to pay closer formal attention
to the work done in this area by Husserl and Merleau-Ponty,
as well as by the existentialist Heidegger. These philosophers
regard language, especially the speaking word and the word
being heard, as a basic way in which man keeps open to
reality and develops his community ties with other men.[15]

---

15 Merleau-Ponty's theory of language is the basis for R. C.
Kwant's exposition: *Phenomenology of Language* (Pittsburgh: Du-
quesne University Press, 1965). The distinction between original
speech (personal speaking) and objective or second-level speech
(organized discourse on facts and theories) is stressed by G. Gusdorf,
Speaking (La Parole) (Evanston, Ill.: Northwestern University
Press, 1965), and in the comparison made between the phenomenological and analytical conceptions of language by M. Dufrenne,
Language and Philosophy (Bloomington: Indiana University Press,
1963). As he moved into the areas of ethics, esthetics, and religion,
Ludwig Wittgenstein had to wrestle with the translinguistic, experiential reference of language, as it speaks in the personal form of
witness to reality. See Wittgenstein's "A Lecture on Ethics," and
F. Waismann's "Notes on Talks with Wittgenstein," *The Philosophical Review*, 74 (1965), 3–16; also, L. Wittgenstein, *Lectures
and Conversations on Aesthetics, Psychology and Religious Belief*

This view of the language activity is not so very far removed from the position of the later Wittgenstein, who sees language also in its humanistic import. The more we probe into the developments on language in the two philosophical traditions, the more we find the creative minds coming to interpret language in terms of man's opening to, and constant practical engagement with, the living world. Differences that immediately crop up between the more dramatic and metaphysical interpretation made by the phenomenologists and the more subdued and restricted interpretation made by the analysts cannot obscure the discovery of some firm common ground of inquiry.

One specific question where the two groups can be observed facing the common human evidence is that of usage involving the language of bodiliness. Both traditions have mounted severe critiques of Cartesian dualism, taken not only metaphysically but also as a careless application of thing-terms to the reality of man. But it is the experience of both groups that, once we are placed on guard against dualistic category-mistakes, the problem still remains of making some discerning use of the language of bodily being and that of reflectivity. Distinctions are still needed in speaking significantly about our own body, both in function of our individual reality and as distinct from the nonhuman bodily world. The precise relationships established by man with the rest of the natural world, in virtue of his capacity for inquiry and for technological reshaping, have to be examined in reference to his talk about embodying human meanings in his conduct and in the environment. Not only naturalism but also phenomenology and analytic philosophy in their attentiveness to the significances of language are thus held together within

(Berkeley and Los Angeles: University of California Press, 1966), pp. 53–64. The comparative theme is developed by P. Ricoeur, "Husserl and Wittgenstein on Language," in *Phenomenology and Existentialism*, pp. 207–17.

the shared domain of human problems. They cannot spring apart from one another on any sure grounds of irrelevance, and the likelihood is that their joint concern about the nature of language will henceforth increase the degree and quality of mutual discussion.

4. Finally, is there any mutuality in their respective conceptions of the philosopher's task? Whether they accept or reject the grand style of earlier types of philosophizing, in practice they are involved in a converging movement because of a minimal, yet basic, agreement about what the philosopher should be doing. Whether he be conceived as elucidating our concepts and modes of talk or as probing into the genesis of our meanings and unifying contexts, his work is essentially that of exploring man's ways with himself and his experienced world. The active modes of human experiencing and acting are manifold and complex, so that they are best investigated by following several paths in philosophy. Nevertheless, there is a center of reference, in human meaningful reality, for both the phenomenological and the analytic ways of reflection. And indeed, the footing in human experience and the discipline of reflectivity may prove to be a sufficiently comprehensive basis for the gradual convergence of other modes of philosophizing in East and West.

14

COMPARATIVE RELIGION: ITS PAST AND FUTURE

MIRCEA ELIADE
University of Chicago

T HE BEGINNINGS OF comparative religion as a discipline took place during the middle of the nineteenth century at the very height of the era of materialistic and positivistic propaganda. Auguste Comte published his *Catéchisme positiviste* in 1852 and his *Système de politique positive* between 1855 and 1858. In 1855 Ludwig Buchner brought out his *Kraft und Stoffe*. The following year Max Müller published his *Essays in Comparative Mythology*, which can be considered the first important book in the field of Comparative Religion. Darwin's *Origin of Species* appeared three years later, and in 1862 Herbert Spencer issued his *First Principles*.

The new discoveries, hypotheses, and theories that the learned world took up from these works with passionate interest rapidly became very popular. One of the best sellers of the epoch was Ernst Haeckel's book, *Natürliche Schöpfungsgeschichte*. Issued in 1868, it went through more than twenty editions before the end of the century and was translated into a dozen languages. While Haeckel's book was furiously reprinted and translated, and Herbert Spencer was elaborating his *System of Synthetic Philosophy* (1860–96),

[245]

the new discipline of the history of religions (or comparative religion) was making rapid progress. In his *Lectures on the Science of Language* (2d ser., 1864), Max Müller introduced his theory concerning solar mythology among the Aryans—a theory grounded in his belief that the myths were born from a "disease of language." In 1871 Edward Burnett Tylor published his *Primitive Culture*, brilliantly trying to reconstruct the origin and evolution of religious experiences and religious beliefs. Tylor identified the first stage of religion with what he called animism: the belief that Nature is animated, that is, has a soul. From animism evolved polytheism, and polytheism finally gave way to monotheism.

I do not intend to recall all the important dates in the history of the scientific study of religion during the second half of the nineteenth century.[1] But this new discipline followed the general pattern imposed by the *Zeitgeist:* the positivistic approach to the "facts" and the search for the "origins," for the very beginnings of religion. Max Müller thought that the Rig-Veda reflects a primordial phase of Aryan religion and consequently one of the most archaic stages of religious beliefs and mythological creations. But already in the early 1870s the French Sanskrit scholar Abel Bergaigne proved that the Vedic hymns, far from being the spontaneous and naïve expressions of a naturalistic religion, were the product of a highly learned and sophisticated class of ritualistic priests.

Scholarly discussion about the Vedas was only an episode in the long and dramatic battle to identify "the origin of religion." A brilliant and learned writer, Andrew Lang, contributed decisively to the demolition of the mythological reconstructions of Max Müller. Two of Lang's most successful works, *Custom and Myth* (1883) and *Modern Mythology* (1897) were drawn up from articles in which he discredited

[1] Cf. Mircea Eliade, "The Quest for the 'Origins' of Religion," *History of Religions*, 4 (1964), 154–69.

Max Müller's ideas with the aid of E. B. Tylor's theories. But a year after the publication of *Modern Mythology*, in 1898, Andrew Lang brought out another book, *Making of Religion*, in which he rejected Tylor's view that the origin of religion is to be found in animism. Lang based his arguments on the presence of a belief in High Gods among some very primitive peoples, such as the Australians and the Andamanese. Tylor held that such a belief could not possibly be original, that the idea of God developed from the belief in nature-spirits and the cult of ancestor ghosts. But Andrew Lang found among the Australians and Andamanese neither ancestor worship nor nature cults.

This unexpected and antievolutionistic claim, that a High God was not at the end of the religious history but at the beginnings, did not greatly impress the contemporary scholarly milieu. It is true that Andrew Lang did not master his documentation thoroughly and in a discussion with Hartland he was compelled to surrender portions of his earlier thesis. Besides, he had the misfortune to be an excellent and versatile writer, the author of a volume of poetry, among other works. And literary gifts usually arouse the scholars' suspicions.

However, Andrew Lang's conception of the primitive High God is significant for other reasons. In the last years of the nineteenth century and the first years of the twentieth, animism ceased to be considered the first stage of religion. Two new theories were proclaimed in that period. They might be called preanimistic, because both of them claimed that they identified a more archaic stage of religion than that described by animism. The first theory is that of Andrew Lang, postulating a belief in a High God at the beginnings of religion. Though almost ignored in England, this hypothesis, corrected and completed, was later on accepted by Graebner and a host of Continental scholars.

Unfortunately, one of the most learned ethnologists of our

time, Wilhelm Schmidt, elaborated the hypothesis of the primitive belief in High Gods into a rigid theory of a primordial monotheism (*Urmonotheismus*). I say unfortunately because Schmidt, though a very able scholar, was also a Catholic priest, and the scientific world suspected him of apologetic intentions. Furthermore, Schmidt was a thorough rationalist, and tried to prove that the idea of God had been grasped by primitive men strictly through causalistic thinking. As Schmidt was publishing the monumental volumes of his *Ursprung der Gottesidee* (1912–1955), however, the Western world witnessed the irruption of quite a number of irrationalist philosophies and ideologies. Bergson's *Élan vital*, Freud's discovery of the unconscious, Lévy-Bruhl's investigations of what he called the prelogical, mystical mentality, Rudolf Otto's *Das Heilige*, as well as the artistic revolutions of dada and surrealism—these mark some of the important events in the history of modern irrationalism. Thus, very few ethnologists and historians of religions could accept Schmidt's rationalist explanation of the discovery of the idea of God.

On the contrary, the epoch running roughly from 1900 to 1920 was dominated by the second preanimistic theory, that of *mana*, that is, the belief in an indistinct and impersonal magico-religious force. It was especially the British anthropologist Marret who insisted on the preanimistic character of the belief in *mana*, showing that this magico-religious experience does not presuppose the concept of a soul and, consequently, represents a more archaic stage than Tylor's animism.[2]

What interests us in this vivid opposition of hypotheses on the origin of religion is the preoccupation with the "primordial." Both preanimistic theories—that of the primordial belief in a High God and that of an original experience of

2 Cf. Mircea Eliade, "The History of Religions in Retrospect: 1912–1962," *The Journal of Bible and Religion*, 30 (1963), 98–109.

the sacred as an impersonal force—maintained that they had reached a deeper level of religious history than Tylor's animism. As a matter of fact, both theories claimed that they had disclosed *the very beginnings* of religion.

Freud also thought that, with the aid of psychoanalysis, he had reached the "primordial" phase of human culture and religion. As is well known, he identified the origin of religion and culture in a primeval murder, more exactly in the first patricide. For Freud, God was merely the sublimated physical father who was slain by his expelled sons. This astonishing explanation was universally criticized and rejected by all responsible ethnologists, from Kroeber to Malinowski and from Boas to Schmidt. But Freud neither renounced nor modified his theory.

While Freud was correcting the proofs of *Totem und Tabu*, to be issued in book form the following year (1913), Émile Durkheim published his *Formes élémentaires de la vie religieuse*. Durkheim, too, was certain that, applying the sociological method, one can grasp the "origin" of religion; for him, religion was a projection of social experience. Studying the Australians, he noticed that the totem symbolizes sacredness and the clan at the same time. He concluded that sacredness (or "God") and the social group are one and the same thing. Durkheim's explanation of the nature and origin of religion was emphatically criticized by a great number of outstanding ethnologists.

Schmidt, Freud, and Durkheim were the last authors to claim that they knew how religion originated and for what reasons and purposes. Such a belief is no longer shared by the historian of religion. He knows by now that he is unable to reach the "origin" of religion. What happened in the beginning, *ab origine*, is no longer a problem for the historian of religion, though conceivably it might be one for the theologian or the philosopher. Almost before he was aware of it, the historian of religions found himself in a cultural milieu quite different from that of Max Müller and Tylor, or even that of Frazer and Marret. It was a new environment nourished by Nietzsche and Marx, Dilthey, Croce, and Ortega, and later on by Heidegger and Sartre; an environment in which the fashionable cliché was not *nature* but *history*, not "origin and development" but temporality and historicity.

The discovery of the historicity of man helped the historians of religions to get rid of the last remnants of angelism and idealism. We now take more seriously the fact that man belongs to *this* world, that he is not a spirit imprisoned in matter. To know that man is always conditioned is to discover that he is equally a creative being. He responds creatively to the challenge of the cosmic, psychological, or historical conditionings. For that reason we no longer accept the naturalistic explanations of human cultures and religions. To give only an example, we know now that primitive man did not—and, as a matter of fact, could not—have a naturistic religion. In the time of Max Müller and Tylor the scholars used to speak of naturistic cults and of fetishism, meaning that primitive man adored natural objects. But the veneration of cosmic objects is not "fetishism." It is not the tree, the spring, or the stone that is venerated *but the sacred that is manifested through these cosmic objects*. This understanding of the archaic man's religious experience is the result of the broadening of our historical consciousness.

In sum, a religious phenomenon cannot be understood outside of its "history," that is, outside of its cultural and socioeconomic contexts. There is no such thing outside of history as a "pure" religious datum. For there is no such thing as a human datum that is not at the same time a historical datum. Every religious experience is expressed and transmitted in a particular historical context. But admitting the historicity of religious experiences does not imply that they are reducible to nonreligious forms of behavior. Stating that a religious datum is always a historical datum does not mean that it is reducible to a nonreligious history—for example, to an economic, social, or political history. We must never lose sight of one of the fundamental principles of modern science: *the scale creates the phenomenon.* Henri Poincaré asked, not without irony: "Would a naturalist who had never studied the elephant except through the microscope consider that he had an adequate knowledge of the creature?" The microscope reveals the structure and mechanism of cells, which structure and mechanism are exactly the same in all multicellular organisms. The elephant is certainly a multicellular organism, but is that all that it is? On the microscopic scale, we might hesitate to answer. On the scale of human vision, which at least has the advantage of presenting the elephant as a zoological phenomenon, there can be no doubt about the reply.

The *homo religiosus* represents the "total man"; hence comparative religion must become a total discipline, in the sense that it must use, integrate, and articulate the results obtained by the various methods of approaching a religious phenomenon. In other words, it must become a *total* and *creative hermeneutics,* since it is called to decipher and explicate every kind of encounter of man with the sacred, from prehistory to our days. We do not doubt that this "creative hermeneutics" will finally be recognized as the royal road of the history of religions. Only then will its role in culture begin to show itself to be important. Such a "total discipline" can open new perspectives to Western thought, to philosophy properly speaking as well as to artistic creations.

Western philosophy cannot contain itself indefinitely within its own tradition without the risk of becoming provincial. Now the historian of religions is able to investigate and elucidate a considerable number of "significant situations" and modalities of existing in the world which are otherwise inaccessible. It is not just a matter of presenting "raw materials," for the philosophers would not know what to do with documents that reflect behavior and ideas too different from those familiar to them.[3] The hermeneutical work ought to be done by the historian of religions himself, for only he is prepared to understand and appreciate the semantic complexity of his documents.

But it is exactly at this point that certain grave misunderstandings have occurred. The rare historians of religions who have wanted to integrate the results of their researches and meditations in a philosophical context have contented themselves with imitating certain fashionable philosophers. In other words, they have compelled themselves to think according to the model of the professional philosophers. And that is a mistake. Neither philosophers nor men of culture are interested in second-hand replicas of their colleagues and favorite authors. In deciding to "think like X" about archaic or oriental thought the historian of religions mutilates and falsifies it. What one expects from him is that he will decipher and elucidate enigmatic behavior and situations—in brief, that he will advance the understanding of man by recovering or reestablishing meanings that have been forgotten, discredited, or abolished. The originality and importance of such contributions reside precisely in their exploration and illumination of spiritual universes that are submerged or that are accessible only with great difficulty. It would be not only illegitimate but ineffectual to disguise archaic and exotic symbols, myths, and ideas in a form already familiar to contemporary philosophers.

This is the reason we have said that a historico-religious

3 It suffices to examine what some rare contemporary philosophers interested in the problems of myth and religious symbolism have done with the "materials" they have borrowed from ethnologists or historians of religions in order to renounce this (illusory) division of labor.

creative hermeneutics would be able to stimulate, nourish, and renew philosophical thought. From a certain point of view, one could say that a new *Phenomenology of the Mind* awaits elaboration by taking account of all that the history of religions is capable of revealing to us. There would be important books to write on modes of existing in the world or on the problems of time, death, and dream, based on documents that the historian of religions has at his disposal.[4] These problems have passionate interest for the philosophers, poets, and art critics. Some of them have read the historians of religions and have utilized their documents and interpretations. It is not their fault if they have not profited from these readings as they expected.

In brief, the history of religions affirms itself as both a "pedagogy," in the strong sense of that term, for it is susceptible of *changing* man, and as a *source of creation* of "cultural values," whatever may be the expression of these values, historiographic, philosophic, or artistic. It seems difficult to believe that, living in a historical moment like ours, the historians of religions will not take account of the creative possibilities of their discipline. How to assimilate *culturally* the spiritual universes that Africa, Oceania, and Southeast Asia open to us? All these spiritual universes have a religious origin and structure. If one does not approach

---

[4] There is, above all, urgent need to get rid of many clichés still encumbering contemporary understanding—for example, Feuerbach's and Marx's celebrated interpretation of religion as alienation. As one knows, Feuerbach and Marx proclaimed that religion estranges man from the earth, prevents him from becoming completely human, and so on. But even if this were correct, such a critique of religion could be applied only to late forms of religiosity such as those of post-Vedic India or of Judeo-Christianity—that is, religions in which the element of "other-worldness" plays an important role. Alienation and estrangement of man from the earth are unknown and, moreover, inconceivable in all religions of the cosmic type, "primitive" as well as oriental; in this case (that is to say, in the overwhelming majority of religions known to history) the religious life consists exactly in exalting the solidarity of man with life and nature.

them in the perspective of the history of religions, they will disappear as spiritual universes; they will be reduced to *facts* about social organizations, economic regimes, epochs of precolonial and colonial history, and so on. In other words, they will not be grasped as *spiritual creations;* they will not enrich Western and world culture; they will serve to augment the number, already terrifying, of *documents* classified in archives, awaiting electronic computers to take them in charge.

15

CHRISTIANITY AND THE
NEW EARTH*

KARL RAHNER, S.J.
University of Münster

T HE BASIC imperative running through the whole of the
*Pastoral Constitution on the Church in the Modern
World* issued by the Second Vatican Council is the sum-
mons to the people of the Church to work together to bring
modern human existence in all its dimensions to a form more
worthy of man. This imperative arises—the point is crucial
—out of the Council's ultimate Christian understanding of
human existence, not because the people of the Church are
Christians and men *besides*, but precisely because the people
of the Church are Christians. The task they share with all
men of good will (including even atheists) is to be accom-
plished out of their properly Christian faith, their eschatological hope, and their love for God and man—a love given to
them by God.

This Constitution does not purport to say—or at least
so it seems in many texts that will have to be considered
more exactly a bit later—that this basic Christian attitude
represents merely some sort of special motivation for seeing
through the already given task, that Christianity furnishes an

* Translated by Francis J. Goetz, S.J., with the collaboration of
Clyde Lee Miller, S.J.

ideological driving force or a new, additional, yet merely formal obligation, while the concrete actuality of the task remains untouched by this motive and these new obligations. The basic Christian attitude would then be fashioned from knowledge that is purely within the world, based on philosophy and the natural law, knowledge of a concrete, practical character. Hence such knowledge would at most have to be protected from error by revelation—with moral necessity in the sense of Vatican I. Rather the Constitution states, for example—to anticipate more exact references—that Christians are to imbue the fabric of secular life with their eschatological hope. Thus the characteristically Christian way of taking up the secular task does not consist solely in a Christian's so shaping the world in accord with principles based on the natural law that Christianity has enough room to develop its properly religious, "other-worldly" mission. Such an aim could be achieved by no more than a philosophical pluralism that assured tolerance and freedom in a society.

How can the task of fashioning a world more worthy of man be the common task of all men of good will? How can any consensus regarding this task be reached among all men if the Christians of the Church still interpret the task as calling for action by Christians which is directed to ends materially different from those of other men? Or is this materially different Christian character of the secular task—a secular task whose exact nature is itself not yet clear or determinate—denied again by the Council's Constitution when this Constitution states, more explicitly than the social encyclicals of the popes from Leo XIII to Pius XII, that the Church can furnish no neat recipe for the concrete shaping of the world and of history and that working out concrete plans and directives is rather the common task of all responsible men? Do we find in this Constitution a veiled and unresolved ambiguity? Or is it simply a matter of fact that there are concretely a great many common tasks and preliminary moves toward a "better world" necessarily shared by Christians and non-Christians alike, even if the initial concept of a this-worldly goal and the more or less ultimate tasks concluding the work are materially different for Christians and non-Christians in meaning and deed? In such a case the distinction marking off the Christian's task from that of others could be left to be worked out at some later time.

The difficulty, which still needs clarification, does not derive simply from postulating a common task that Christians share with non-Christians as such. Indeed, one could think that perhaps such a common task can exist, since in the case of non-Christians too the final dynamism powering their historical actions and decisions is, of course, grace, even if they do not know this. One could say further that in every pluralistic society (which is recognized by all as favoring common action) cooperation is to be secured through the interaction of divergent historical drives. So it should not be astonishing if Christians stake their own notion of the future on competitive open dialogue.

II

The difficulty lies rather in the matter itself: do we have, indeed can we as Christians have, a properly Christian, this-worldly ideology regarding the future? Insofar as the question does not refer to general "natural-law" or "Christian" principles—which do exist—but to a concrete program, to clear, concrete imperatives (for today and tomorrow, even though they always remain open to the larger future), the official Church clearly cannot proclaim such an absolute, concrete program.[1] It is not authorized to do this, it is not capable, and makes no claim to be so. Such observations,

---

[1] Karl Rahner, "Grenzen des Amtskirche," *Schriften zur Theologie*, VI (Einsiedeln: 1965), 499–520.

however, do not simply answer the question in the negative. For it is at least still conceivable[2] that the Church find and choose such a concrete program, acting as the concrete people of God in a concrete, as it were, "political" decision, even if this is not at all a mere deduction from natural-law and Christian principles.

What such a choice would mean for the individual Christian can remain an open question here, that is, whether as an individual he has to be "for" the declared choice. Open, too, are the questions of how such a "politico"-historical decision of the Church is concretely brought about and how it functions to form the will of the whole profane society, of a state, of a group of nations, or how it fails so to function. It might also be conceivable that the official Church would later more clearly articulate such a basic decision—at first hit upon almost instinctively and held unreflectively—regarding the concrete, earthly future of mankind, and that the Church would proclaim it in the form of a "directive" to be clearly distinguished from doctrine and commandment. If something like this is considered fundamentally possible,[3] that is, if some middle ground is recognized as occupied by neither the Church in its officially constituted authority nor by individual Christians acting only as individual members of profane society though under Christian "inspiration," in this case there would be place for such a specifically Christian, this-worldly program and decision for the future,

2 With regard to the following distinction see the *Pastoral Constitution on the Church in the Modern World*, Nos. 43, 74, 75, 76. References to this document will be quoted simply by number hereafter. Other conciliar documents will be quoted with their respective titles.

3 For more detailed treatment, see Karl Rahner, "Zur theologischen Problematic einer Pastoralkonstitution," in *Volk Gottes*: Zum Kirchenverständnis der katholischen, evangelischen und angliskanischen Theologie, R. Baumer and H. Dolch, eds.: (Freiburg: 1967), pp. 683–703.

however much the program might or might not be carried out in fact.

Is there such a future that Christianity itself can concretely project out of the present? When the pastoral Constitution says[4] that the future and its world must be "more humane," "more just," and "more peaceful" than the present, that it must be penetrated with the justice and love that make possible the free development of every man, must allow the unity of men as a family of brothers to grow, that it must strive harder against the spirit of egoism and other sinfulness, when such basic principles are also detailed for more concrete areas—to promote a just and humane policy toward families, structuring of the economy, efforts for peace, and so on—then of course we are presented with a goal that Christianity, that is, Christian faith and God's command, calls for. But these principles still do not proclaim any specifically Christian content for this desired future.

This is also the case when it is stated that the future shaping of society must be penetrated by the Christian spirit. Again, little more is clearly added when the unity of love for God and for one's neighbor is emphasized or when the significance of revelation for the effective recognition of human dignity is praised. One could well think that the stress on the idea that Christians share the earthly task with all men of good will (for example, *Pastoral Constitution*, Ch. i, No. 21 and *passim*) points to a negative answer to our question as to whether there is a specifically Christian earthly future. And the same negative answer is suggested because the "integral" (otherworldly) vocation of man is distinguished from his human tasks (No. 11) when the "building of the world" "serves the whole vocation of man" (No. 35), because the growth of God's kingdom and

[4] With regard to the following see the *Pastoral Constitution*, Nos. 11, 15, 21, 23, 24, 26, 37, 38, 40, 41, 43, 55, 57, 58, 61, 63, 76.

earthly progress are distinguished as two separate things (Nos. 36, 38, 39, 42, 43), because the relative autonomy of the order of creation (Nos. 34, 36, 39, 41, 59, 67) is stressed although its otherworldly connections are emphasized, and because response to the world and striving toward the native city of heaven are distinguished and the duality of the orders of knowledge is underlined (No. 59), and so on.

III

But now the other side of the evidence must also be considered. What does it mean to say that there exists a unity of mankind which on the one hand Christ founded (No. 32) and which has to grow until the day of fulfillment (No. 32), but which on the other hand does not seem to be strictly identical with the Church as such since mankind as a whole is to be brought to the unity of the family of God?[5] What does it mean when the kerygma of the Gospel is said to be already rooted in the human situation to some extent before this fact becomes manifest through verbal creativity (No. 62)? What does it mean to emphasize that mankind strives toward a future in which humanity itself will become a sacrifice pleasing to God (No. 38), and to say that the earthly service rendered by men prepares the "material of the kingdom of God" (No. 38)? Several times at the Council there was talk of the "new earth" and the "new heaven." Of course this "new earth" is represented as the eschatological gift of God himself and thus is not merely the result of earthly progress ("progressus terrenus," No. 39). Yet it is also not simply something to replace what

5 See Nos. 40, 43; *Lumen gentium*, No. 28. There is no talk here of the desired extension of the Church to the whole of humanity and in this sense of the unity of God's family ("unitas familiae Dei"), since the "growing body of the new human family" is not only to be thought of quantitatively nor is it identical with the Church, and yet it is a foreshadowing ("adumbratio") of the future world (*cf.* No. 39).

has gone before. It does not merely push this aside and do away with it, but is a transformation of the previous world ("transformatio mundi," No. 38; "universi transformandi," No. 39). However, this world that is to be thus transformed does not seem to be only the one that God himself has created (taken in its simple, substantial existence). For it is stated (No. 39) that not just love will remain but its *work* ("opus") as well and that we will "find again" the results of our labor ("industriae nostrae fructus"), the consequences of human activity (for they are thought of as "purified.") So the world is conceived as something to be transformed, something man himself has created in the "carrying forward of creation" (Nos. 34, 57). This "carrying forward of God's creation" is frequently referred to, even if it is viewed as the execution of God's creative will somehow distinct from his supernatural, salvific will.

The divine love is also the law of the "transformation of the world" (No. 38), and to it a universal brotherhood ("fraternitas universalis") pertains which apparently does not consist simply of the Church as such (*ibid.*). Eschatological hope is to be impressed into the structures of secular life itself (*Lumen gentium*, No. 35). If the "renewal of the world" is thus already irrevocably established and is already anticipated in this age ("in hoc saeculo") in a real way (*Lumen gentium*, No. 48), then this anticipated presence of the eschatological "renewal of the world" is not given merely in the Church, its kerygma and cult alone, but also in the structures of secular life. Only thus can mankind at present devise a sketchy notion of the world of the future (No. 39). The hints found in the Constitution should certainly not be overinterpreted. The Constitution does not clearly resolve the alternative between what we can call "a secular shape for the future influenced by the Christian spirit but of a purely earthly and passing kind" and "a Christian shaping of the future created by men and possessing ultimate significance." Nor is it really clear how to respond to these alternatives. Yet the Constitution, itself groping and hesitant, brings us to face the question the alternatives raise.

IV

Perhaps the real question has now become clear: Is the world that man himself creates only the "material" for his moral testing, remaining in itself morally indifferent? Will the world simply disappear when the definitive kingdom of God arrives? The thrust of this question becomes clearer when we note that this world is no longer the milieu provided by God himself for man's moral activity, but it is a world raised to the second power: man himself creates it in the course of history as the fulfillment of God's creation committed to him. Can this world, thus understood, still be compared to the rush baskets that the old monks of the Scythian desert wove during the day and unwove in the evening in order to pass their time without sinning while they awaited the eternity of an anticipated but as yet totally unrealized future? Or does this second world, the world of man's creation, enter into the eschaton proper, even if it be unimaginably "transformed"? Does the "new earth" come down from heaven (even though to a virtually neutral "ground" that God once created and that will be constituted by the identity in substance of man's original mortal body with his glorified body and because the material world thereby constituted is no more given up than man's original mortal body is)? Or will the "new earth" be constructed here in time by men? Should we understand "new" earth or an earth that is "renewed" (of course, in the infinity of the eternally young God)?

Earlier man could not put the question so clearly. For this world of which we speak did not exist earlier. Early man lived in a world of "nature" that was merely given. What man created himself was small and frail—from the body, which died, to the relatively few products of cultural activity. All this seemed merely fuel for the coming world conflagration that could leave behind only ashes. The real eschatological outcome of history could be glimpsed beforehand only in the ethical quality of the immortal "soul" taken along into the "beyond." The "resurrection of the body" was expected, of course; one could picture the wounds of Christ's glorified body remaining as the victory marks of his life history. Somehow near the edge of consciousness—and only there—the question we have posed was alive. As the pastoral Constitution indicates, the question has not yet been clearly worked out as a question even today. Nor is it merely a scholastic subtlety, as when De Broglie racks his brains over whether resurrected bodies can still eat. For this question is—though in a pointed form—a question about the more exact relation between Christian eschatological hope and the modern ideology of the future, that is, of a future Utopia (in a neutral meaning of the term). Are we accomplishing our ultimate end if, just, loving, and obedient to God's commission to us regarding this world, we have fulfilled his creative design? Is fulfillment such that the moral element[6] of history remains meta-empirical in its deepest foundations? Will such a morality constitute the final stage of men and matter, which have been created solely by God himself? Or does material, corporal history also help constitute this definitive state,[7] even though by means of death and radical transformation?

This question is not without importance for the relationship of Marxism and Christianity, for the Christian inter-

---

[6] The ultimate moral quality of history, as it exists before God, cannot be read by us from history with certainty.

[7] This holds as a positive Christian view in any case and was always clearly known by Christianity.

pretation of history, and for many other matters in the
Christian understanding of man's existence. As Christians,
we are not struggling with a naïve form of Marxism which
simply exploits the individual as material for a future
society and history. It would indeed be a kind of Marxist
faith either to consider oneself able directly to complete
"the kingdom of God" by oneself, or to view the future only
as the lure of history, a lure always unattainable, receding
into the indeterminate, leading to an unfinished whole
grasped by no one.

We Christians—even granted the proviso that one can
take something too seriously and so ruin it—have to allow
ourselves to be asked by Marxism how seriously we really
take the world that is committed to our making. Is it
ultimately only indifferent material on which we exercise
our virtues? Would this be to take it seriously enough?
Does it not become in fact indifferent insofar as one could
also exercise the same virtues in a world that is kept re-
actionary—especially the virtue of patience vis-à-vis a mean,
annoying, unjust world? If we Christians were to respond to
this question, we could not invent our own situations for
protecting the kingdom of heaven, but rather we would have
to test our heavenly virtues, which alone are "abiding," on
the "material" that is sent to us now in the course of the
world. And since this world changes, we must ask ourselves
once more why it should be that in dealing with change the
definitive virtues to be exercised are those whose "material"
and "objective" results fall back into transiency, into what is
no more. This question is not meant to be clever or over-
played. For it remains true in any case that concrete history
in its corporeality is the place where the definitive stage of
existence and the absolute future is actualized. In any case,
too, all that the Council said holds true about Christians' responsibility for the world and about the error in an artificial
opposition between the Christian's integral (and hence "other-

worldly") vocation and his task in the world. But perhaps it will be evident that the question we have posed is also not without import in view of the intellectual situation today, in which Christianity has to make its message intelligible.

V

But can this question be answered at all and how is it to be answered?

First, the following is clear: The kingdom of God, the definitive stage which ends and "cancels" history, is something of itself due really to come about. This stage is not just a constant lure for history, its merely asymptotic goal which would simply function to keep history moving. This definitive stage will not be present as a simple last state and end result of history planned and effected by man but will be the act of God. And this act is of course to be regarded—here just as in the history of nature and the world—as the self-transcendence of human history (divine, free, quite incalculable from the starting point of our action). History and its completed final stage are always distinct and separated from one another by that which is experienced in each individual's history as death and entails a radical "transformation"; this last affects the whole of history just as death does the history of the individual. "The time of the consummation of the world and of mankind is unknown, as is the manner of transformation of the whole world" (No. 39). Therefore the statement about the permanence of history—not only in its meta-empirical ethical quality but also in its historical result—is not presented on quite the same terms as the statement about the radical transformation of history into the unknown and into the openness of the absolute future which is God himself. It is impossible to form a concept of history in its permanent definitive state. Every description—we are warned in Matthew 22:30 ("At the resurrection they will neither marry nor be given in marriage . . .")—would be a pseudo-Christian apocalyptic and not a Christian eschatology. Even the attempt to imagine a glorified body as it will be leads to contradictions; this would be all the more the case if one wished to make the same attempt with respect to the body of mankind, which is gradually forming in its own history.

On the other hand, one may not take the opposite position, holding that, besides having eschatological validity and permanence, the end point of mankind's history also would have absolutely *no* concrete reference to mankind's history itself. For the same objection could be made regarding the corporeity of an individual's history. No single time of life can be *the* model of the definitive state of the body, and yet Christian tradition has considered this ultimate state as bringing one's whole concrete history to a glorified manifestation when it becomes actual.

The two propositions about the ultimate validity of history and about its radical transformation for the present remain unresolved for us in a fundamental dialectic that keeps the future open and allows the present to retain its basic importance. Both propositions are hermeneutical principles as well as statements of fact. But, given these presuppositions, what more can be said? History itself constructs its own ultimate fulfillment. What is permanent is the work of concrete love in history; love remains as what is done by men and not merely a moral distillate that history leaves behind as its exhausted "residue." History itself enters into the fullness (*Endgültigkeit*) of God himself, not only of man, who acts once in history and then after his role has been played (as in Hugo Von Hoffmannsthal's "Everyman") leaves it behind as what has become unreal.

Why can it be said that history enters into God's own fullness? Because the Word of God has himself both made and endured history. Were our thesis entirely false, then he would have had to do away with his "role" entirely. But he remains forever the God-Man, and his humanity is not merely rewarded with glory but remains above all his own, which would be really superfluous if this thesis were not true. The opposite contention basically leads to an intolerable division of "soul from body" and of noumenon from phenomenon. True human "history" in freedom constructs of its very nature its definitive stage and is not merely rewarded with it. The conclusive stage is not placed "behind" the history in which events occur for which we are responsible, even if this conclusive stage is not evident on the surface of reality and can never be judged by us. The correctness of our thesis is also suggested by a positive answer to the question whether the ethical—without prejudice to the fact that it has to be done as the work of freedom—*is* not just what becomes more concrete in history, whether it does not have its significance in and from history. So history itself must have an ultimate meaning if the ethical is to have it as well.

VI

If then the history made by man has ultimate significance as event and as result, then the basis and presupposition for this fact become apparent. Even this "worldly world" that as such remains profane still basically manifests in itself a hidden Christian element. The mandate of creation and its completion appear as an inner moment of the single, complete, redeeming, and divinizing will of God for a world in which his self-communication takes place, and they get their final meaning and concrete shape from this whole. So they are fixed precisely in their proper worldly character until their consummation.

All this, however, still says nothing with regard to what makes up the concrete Christian character of the this-worldly realization of the future. Because the answer to this question is so difficult, one should not think that it cannot be ascertained. As was mentioned earlier, however, because the historical action of non-Christians regarding the future is also under the dynamism of grace, this more precise question cannot be posed in face of the unresolved dilemma confronting us, which demands that we either point out some Christian feature in this future which is advocated only by the "explicit" Christians, or that we recognize what is sought after as merely "human." For that reason (and over and beyond it) it is possible that the Christian "significance" and the final Christian root of a historical reality that is to come (social, political, and so on) will first manifest itself when it is already present and thus can be interpreted reflexively. Such a reality manifests itself for example in the growing unity of mankind which is frequently referred to in the pastoral Constitution and which is in fact presupposed for a Church that is really worldwide. Another example might perhaps be the obviously growing openness to the future and its planning—the dialectic of increased planning and of unplanned contingencies that as such are formally and explicitly anticipated. In this dialectic—insoluble for us —God's absolute future perhaps shows itself in silent presence. The Christian shaping of the this-worldly dynamism of the future thus ultimately does not depend on Christians setting up concrete societal, political, social, and other demands special to themselves and to no one else. Such a conclusion would make it clear that at heart the Christian does not have two tasks that would be held together only by a "moral" bond effected by one's obligation to both and thus only by the abstract, moral significance that his secular task would have for eternity.[8]

[8] For further clarification of what is set forth here, see the author's treatment of these problems: "Marxistische Utopie und Christliche Zukunft des Menschen," *Schriften zur Theologie*, as cited *supra*, pp. 77–88; also his "Experiment Mensch," "Christlicher Humanismus," and "Zum Problem der genetischen Manipulation," *ibid.*, VIII (1967).

NOTES ON THE CONTRIBUTORS

SIR ERIC ASHBY, master of Clare College at Cambridge University since 1959, is former chairman of the Nigerian Universities Commission. Born in London, he earned his doctorate in science at the University of London and did research in experimental botany and held professorships in Sydney, Australia, and Manchester, England. During World War II he served as counsellor and acting minister at the Australian Legation in Moscow, and from 1950 to 1959 was President of Queen's University, Belfast. A member of the Central Advisory Council for Science and Technology and the University Grants Committee, he has had fifteen years of experience in advisory work for universities in tropical Africa and was President of the British Association for the Advancement of Science in 1963 and Godkin Lecturer at Harvard University in 1964. He is a Fellow of the Royal Society and holds honorary degrees from fourteen universities. His published works include *Environment and Plant Development* (1931), *Technology and the Academics* (1958), *African Universities and Western Tradition* (1964), and *Universities: British, Indian, African* (1966).

JAMES R. BRIGHT is professor of business administration at the Harvard University Graduate School of Business Administration and a specialist in the relations between technology and business. A native of Pittsburgh, Pennsylvania, he studied at Lehigh and Columbia universities. After holding a position as test engineer for the General Electric Company, he served five and one-half years in the Army and then as an editor for the McGraw-Hill Publishing Company and the Cahners Publishing Company for eight years. He joined the faculty at Harvard in 1954. He has been editor of *Product Engineering* and *Modern Material Handling* and is the author of *Automation and Management* (1958) and *Research Development, and Technological Innovation* (1964), as well as many papers.

HARLAN CLEVELAND, United States Ambassador to the North Atlantic Treaty Organization, is known the world over as one of the most articulate and informed scholars and writers in the diplomatic corps. Born in New York City, he studied at Princeton University and was a Rhodes scholar at Oxford University. He has served as publisher of *The Reporter* magazine, dean of the Maxwell Graduate School of Citizenship and Public Affairs at Syracuse University, as Assistant Secretary of State for International Organization Affairs, and as a member of the board of trustees of Experiment in International Living. During World War II he was decorated with the U.S. Medal of Freedom and Order of the Crown of Italy for his work as vice president of the Allied Commission in Rome. His books include *The Overseas Americans* (1960), *The Promise of World Tensions* (1961), and *The Obligations of Power* (1966).

JAMES D. COLLINS, professor of philosophy at Saint Louis University, is an internationally known historian of modern philosophy. Born in Holyoke, Massachusetts, he received the degrees of B.A., M.A., and Ph.D. from the Catholic University of America and was a research fellow at Harvard University in 1944-45. He gave the Suarez Lecture at Fordham University in 1953 and the Aquinas Lecture at Marquette University in 1962. In 1963-64 he held a Guggenheim Fellowship. His many scholarly studies on both European and American thinkers include books on *The Existentialists* (1952), *The Mind of Kierkegaard* (1953), *A History of Modern European Philosophy* (1954), *God in Modern Philosophy* (1959), and *The Emergence of Phi-*

losophy of Religion (1967), this last being the Thomas More Lectures, which he gave at Yale University in 1963, now published in enlarged form by Yale University Press.

JOHN T. EDSALL is professor of biological chemistry at Harvard University, where he received his A.B. and M.D. degrees and in 1928 began his teaching career as tutor in biochemical sciences. He was born in Philadelphia, Pennsylvania. A Guggenheim Fellow, he has also been a Fulbright lecturer at Cambridge University and the University of Tokyo and visiting professor at the Collège de France and has served as consultant to many foundations and research groups. Since 1944 he has edited *Advances in Protein Chemistry* and since 1958 has been editor of the *Journal of Biological Chemistry*. Known especially for his own research on proteins, he is the author of a large number of scholarly publications, including *Biophysical Chemistry* (with J. Wyman, 1958).

MIRCEA ELIADE is Sewell L. Avery Distinguished Service Professor of History of Religions at the University of Chicago. He was born in Bucharest, Romania, where he received his doctorate from the University of Bucharest. He subsequently studied at the University of Calcutta. He has lectured at the universities of Bucharest, Rome, Lund, Marburg, Munich, Frankfurt, Strasbourg, Padua, and Paris and has served as cultural attaché at the Romanian legations in London and Lisbon. His many books include *Techniques du Yoga* (1948), *Le Chamanisme* (1951), *The Myth of the Eternal Return* (1954), *Patterns of Comparative Religions* (1958), and *The Forge and the Crucible* (1962).

GYORGY KEPES is a painter and since 1946 has been professor of visual design at the Massachusetts Institute of Technology. He became the first Director of the Center for Advanced Visual Studies when this center began operation at the Massachusetts Institute of Technology in the fall of 1967. He is a native of Hungary, where he studied at the

Royal Academy of Fine Arts. His paintings have been exhibited in Budapest, Berlin, New York City, Chicago, San Francisco, Cleveland, London, and elsewhere, and he has written widely on man's visual environment and its effects on consciousness and culture. He is editor of *Visual Arts Today* and of the six-volume series entitled *Vision and Value*, and the author of *Language of Vision* (1944), *The New Landscape* (1956), and many other works.

MARSHALL MCLUHAN is director of the Graduate Center of Culture and Technology at the University of Toronto and was named in 1967 to the Albert Schweitzer Professorship of the Humanities, the State of New York Regents chair assigned to Fordham University. Born in Edmonton, Alberta, Canada, he studied at the universities of Manitoba and of Wisconsin and received his doctorate in English at Cambridge University in 1942. He was instructor in English at Saint Louis University from 1937 to 1944. Well known today to all students of the communications media throughout the world, as well as to a large television audience and to many professional groups to whom he has lectured, he was editor of the pioneering periodical *Explorations* from 1953 to 1959 and is the author of *The Mechanical Bride* (1951), *The Gutenberg Galaxy* (1962), *Understanding Media* (1964), *The Medium Is the Massage* (1967), and other works. *The Gutenberg Galaxy* received the 1963 Canadian Governor General's award for expository prose.

JOHN MACQUARRIE is an Anglican priest and professor of systematic theology at Union Theological Seminary in New York. A native of Scotland, he obtained his degrees from the University of Glasgow, where he also taught theology for nine years before coming to Union Theological Seminary in 1962. He gave the Hastie lectures at the University of Glasgow and the Cooper lectures at Swarthmore College in 1962 and was the John M. English lecturer at the Andover-Newton Divinity School and Birks lecturer at McGill University in 1963. He is author of *An Existentialist Theology*

(1955), *The Scope of Demythologizing* (1960), *Twentieth-Century Religious Thought* (1963), *Studies in Christian Existentialism* (1965), *Principles of Christian Theology* (1966), *God-Talk* (1967), and other works.

CHARLES MUSCATINE is professor of English at the University of California, Berkeley. He was born in Brooklyn, New York, and received his B.A., M.A., and Ph.D. from Yale University. He has held research fellowships from the American Council of Learned Societies and the John Simon Guggenheim Memorial Foundation as well as a Fulbright research fellowship. Known as a distinguished medieval scholar, the author of *Chaucer and the French Tradition* (1957), *The Book of Geoffrey Chaucer* (1963), and other works, he was chairman of the Berkeley faculty's Select Committee on Education and editor and co-author of the Committee's epoch-making report, *Education at Berkeley* (1966).

JOHN T. NOONAN, JR., until September, 1967, professor of law at the University of Notre Dame, is now professor of law at the University of California, Berkeley. Born in Boston, Massachusetts, he studied at Harvard University (B.A., LL.B.), at Cambridge University, and at the Catholic University of America (M.A., Ph.D.). From 1955 to 1961 he practiced law in Boston. He is editor of the *Natural Law Forum*, published at the University of Notre Dame, and has been director of the Notre Dame Natural Law Institute, and a Guggenheim Fellow. His many works include *The Scholastic Analysis of Usury* (1957) and the definitive study *Contraception: A History of Its Treatment by the Catholic Theologians and Canonists* (1965). He has served as chairman of the Brookline Redevelopment Authority, as a member of the Special Staff of the National Security Council, and as consultor to the Papal Commission on Problems of the Family, Population, and Natality, 1965–66.

WALTER J. ONG, S.J., is professor of English at Saint

Louis University. A native of Kansas City, Missouri, he studied at Rockhurst College (B.A.) and worked in commercial positions two years before entering the Society of Jesus (Jesuit order), continuing his studies thereafter at Saint Louis University (M.A., S.T.L.) and Harvard University (Ph.D.). He was ordained a priest in 1946. Twice recipient of a Guggenheim Fellowship, he has also been a Fellow at the Center for Advanced Studies at Wesleyan University (Connecticut). He has served as visiting professor at the University of California and Indiana University, visiting lecturer at the University of Poitiers in France, Macdonald lecturer at McGill University in Canada, Terry lecturer at Yale University in 1963–64, and Berg Professor of English and American Literature at New York University in 1966–67. His many publications include the books *Frontiers in American Catholicism* (1957), *Ramus, Method, and the Decay of Dialogue* (1958), *Ramus and Talon Inventory* (1958), *American Catholic Crossroads* (1959), *The Barbarian Within* (1962), *In the Human Grain* (1967), and *The Presence of the Word* (1967).

KARL RAHNER, S.J., is professor of dogmatic theology and the history of dogma at the University of Münster and was a consultant (*peritus*) at the Second Vatican Council. He was born in Freiburg-im-Breisgau, Germany, and after entering the Society of Jesus (Jesuit order), studied at Pullach, near Munich, at Valkenburg, Holland, at Freiburg, and at Innsbruck, Austria, where he received a doctorate in theology in 1936. He was ordained a priest in 1932. After the Nazis disbanded the Innsbruck Faculty of Theology in 1938, he was engaged in pastoral work in Vienna and Bavaria. He has also been professor of Christian thought and philosophy of religion at the University of Munich. In 1964 he was decorated by the government of Tirol, Austria, for his contribution to learning, and in 1965 received the Reuchlin Prize from the city of Pforzheim. Since 1957 he has been editor, with Joseph Höfer, of the *Lexicon für Theologie und Kirche* as well as editor of the series *Quae-*

stiones Disputatae. His numerous works, many of which are now being translated into English, include *Zür Theologie des Todes* (1958), *Free Speech in the Church* (1959), *Inspiration in the Bible* (1961), and *Amt und Charisma in der Kirche* (1962).

ROBERT C. WEAVER, educator, economist, and author, became the first United States Secretary of Housing and Urban Development in 1966. He had been administrator of the predecessor Housing and Home Finance Agency since 1961. He is a native of Washington, D.C., and holds his B.S., M.A., and Ph.D. degrees from Harvard University, with honorary degrees from more than twenty other institutions. Dr. Weaver entered government service in 1933 and has held many federal posts in national housing, defense, and manpower fields until 1944, when he began an extensive nonfederal career in human relations in Chicago and subsequently as lecturer at Northwestern University. He has been visiting professor at Columbia University Teachers College and New York University and has served as an officer or consultant to a large number of foundations and public agencies. His many publications include the books *Negro Labor: A National Problem* (1946), *The Negro Ghetto* (1948), *The Urban Complex* (1964), and *Dilemmas of Urban America* (1965). He is former chairman of the National Association for the Advancement of Colored People and in 1962 was recipient of its Spingarn Medal.

JERROLD R. ZACHARIAS, Institute professor and professor of physics at Massachusetts Institute of Technology, has enjoyed a double career as a research scientist and as a reformer and vivifier of science teaching in the United States and around the world. He was born in Jacksonville, Florida, and studied at Columbia University (B.A., M.A., Ph.D.). He was a staff member of the Radiation Laboratory at Massachusetts Institute of Technology from 1940 to 1945, divisional head at the University of California Los Alamos laboratory in 1945, and director of the Massachusetts Institute of Technology Laboratory for Nuclear Science and Engineering from 1946 to 1956. He has published papers on science and science education, has been a member of the United States President's Science Advisory Committee, is chairman of the Panel on Educational Research and Development of the President's Science Advisory Committee, and is vice president of Educational Development Center, Incorporated.